40p

LAMMERMUIR

A name that means value
for money—simple, elegant,
satisfying styles for women
who know what they want
at the right price.

Dresses
Skirts
Pinafores
Suits
Coats
Trouser Suits
in a wide choice of
Tartans
Tweeds
Jersey Wool
Crimplene

Garments on display at

87
HAYMARKET TER.,
EDINBURGH

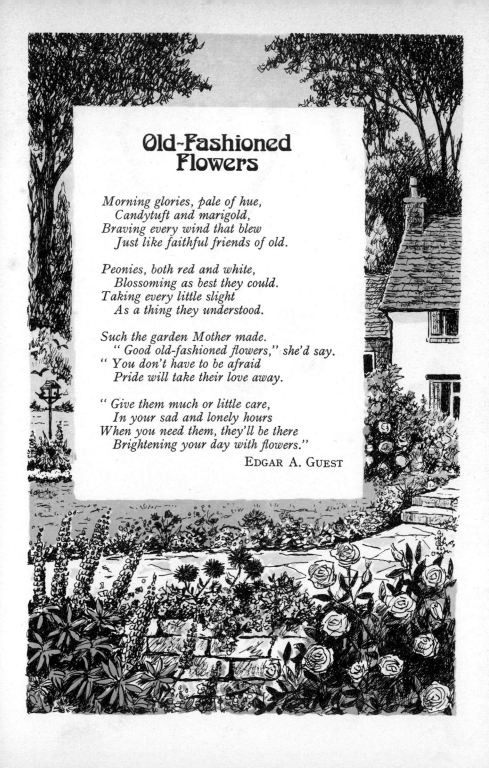

Old-Fashioned Flowers

Morning glories, pale of hue,
  Candytuft and marigold,
Braving every wind that blew
  Just like faithful friends of old.

Peonies, both red and white,
  Blossoming as best they could.
Taking every little slight
  As a thing they understood.

Such the garden Mother made.
  " Good old-fashioned flowers," she'd say.
" You don't have to be afraid
  Pride will take their love away.

" Give them much or little care,
  In your sad and lonely hours
When you need them, they'll be there
  Brightening your day with flowers."

EDGAR A. GUEST

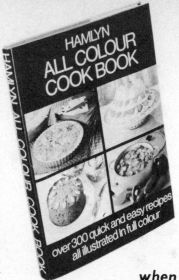

People's Friend Annual

•

CONTENTS

SCOTLOAN
gets you the things you want - without waiting

A car. Improvements to the home. New furniture. We can help you get what you want without waiting, with SCOTLOAN. That's the name of our personal loan service. SCOTLOAN is available from £100 to £1,000 repayable in monthly instalments, and you can have up to 36 months to repay.

SCOTLOAN costs you less than money from most other sources, including H.P. and, with it, you get life assurance as well – at no extra cost.
Call at any branch of Bank of Scotland. And when you do, look into our other Scotservices – all created to help you take a happier view of your money.

BANK OF SCOTLAND
TAKES THE WORRY OUT OF MONEY

So Wishes Do Come True!

JILL ROSSITER stood at the window for several minutes watching the heavy rain. Then she sighed deeply and turned back towards the room to face the debris of last night's party. It had been a really good party, and all the guests had appeared to enjoy themselves thoroughly.

Jill and her mother had worked hard preparing things right up to

BY
Constance
Kay

9

the time the telegram came. Gran had suddenly taken ill, and Mrs Rossiter had to hurry to catch the train to Dunfermline.

" I don't like leaving you with still so much to do," she had said, hastily packing a suitcase. " And then there's the clearing-up tomorrow. Why don't you ring Stella Murray and ask her to come over and help? After all, she suggested the party, didn't she?"

It was true, of course. The party for the Scottish country dancing group in the new town of Glenrogie had been Stella's idea, but, as she pointed out, the rooms in her own house were too small. So Jill, as her best friend, had offered the use of her mother's older house on the outskirts of the town.

Stella, when appealed to by telephone, readily agreed to come early to help with the final chores and, as the following day would be Saturday, promised to stay overnight with Jill and do her share in the morning as well.

But Stella hadn't come early on Friday evening; she had to work late at the office, she said. Moreover, she had brought a new boy friend along to the party and had gone off with him about ten o'clock, completely forgetting her arrangement to stay overnight and help with the clearing-up.

It wasn't the first time Stella Murray had let her friend down, but she was always so penitent afterwards and had such plausible excuses that it was hard for Jill to be angry.

AFTER three or four journeys to the kitchen, each with a tray-load of dirty plates, cups, glasses and cutlery, there was no flat surface left on which to put so much as another spoon.

Jill sat down and considered the situation again. Should she finish tidying up the living-room, empty the ashtrays and vacuum the carpet? Or, as an alternative, begin on the mountains of washing-up? Or should she make herself a pot of coffee and wish hard that a miracle might happen? For under her horoscope sign in the morning paper it said : "A wish will be granted !"

Of course, she didn't really believe it, it was just for fun ! And it didn't necessarily mean your own wish. Still, Jill's grandmother, who came from the Hebrides, firmly believed in wishing, and she would certainly have advised Jill to have a try.

So she clasped her hands, closed her eyes again and wished hard.

There was a ring at the back door bell. Oh, good ! This must be Stella, come to keep her promise ! But the open door revealed a tall young man in a white overall with a large badge embroidered on the breast pocket. It looked like some kind of Indian idol, and Jill stared at it, fascinated. Then she noticed the drop of rain which was running down the dark-brown forelock on to the young man's nose. A nice-shaped, interesting nose, Jill thought, above a smiling but rather nervous mouth.

" Yes?" she asked, and waited.

" Many hands . . ." replied the young man.

" Many hands . . . what?" queried Jill, as he seemed to need some encouragement to go on.

" Many hands make light work !" he said.

" Ay, so they do !" responded Jill brightly. Was this some kind of game, she wondered.

" I mean," the young man continued. " I've brought the machine to demonstrate, as requested.

" Machine? What kind of machine?"

" The Many Hands Dish-washer ! Mrs "—he consulted his notebook— " Mrs Rossiter asked for a demonstration, positively no obligation, you know !"

Jill saw that he was looking at her shortie housecoat, her long fair hair hanging round her shoulders, her face free from make-up, and realised she probably looked about twelve years old. She could almost read his thoughts that this lassie couldn't be Mrs Rossiter.

" Could you fetch your mother?" he asked as Jill looked at him doubtfully. " This is the right house, isn't it ? "

" Mrs Rossiter's my mother, she's been called away suddenly, but . . ." She noticed his very blue eyes straying beyond her to the piles of dirty dishes and her heart gave a big jump.

" You did say positively no obligation? Well, can't you demonstrate to me? I'll give my mother a faithful account when she returns. I'm older than I look, quite responsible, really !" She drew herself up to her full five foot three.

" Anyhow, come in out of the rain, you're getting soaked," she went on earnestly as he still appeared to hesitate. " And take off that wet coat. I'll give you a cup of coffee—if I can find a clean cup. I was just going to make some for myself."

" Oh, thanks ! And I might as well bring the machine in, if you show me where it can stand."

HE disappeared, and Jill frantically cleared one draining board by depositing the crockery on the floor. She selected two cups which didn't look too bad, washed them, and was searching for a tea-towel when the young man reappeared. He was pushing a high trolley with a contraption on it covered by an outsize plastic bag.

" Here we are, madam," he recited in an unnatural, sing-song voice. " Our Many-Hands-Make-Light-Work-Dish-Washer heats the water, washes three times, rinses, dries and polishes ; all at the touch of one small button."

Then he sneezed.

" Bless you !" Jill said. " You'd better get that coat off, the coffee won't be a moment."

There was no room to sit in the kitchen, so she led the way to the living-room and switched on the electric fire there.

The young man looked round the untidy room with surprise and Jill felt an explanation was due. So she told him about the party and about her mother having to go away suddenly ; and how her best friend had let her down.

" Not much of a best friend, I would say," remarked the young man. " I would find another one if I were in your place."

Jill laughed.

"That might not be so easy," she replied, "in a new town like Glenrogie. But how long have you been doing this job?"

"I'm not very good, am I? I'm just filling in while I wait for exam results. If I get a good pass I shall qualify for a position in the research department of the firm."

THEY went back to the kitchen and Jill made another pot of coffee while her unexpected guest loaded the dish-washer, plugged it in, and set it through its programme. When it had switched itself off, his white overall still wasn't dry, so he loaded up the machine again and Jill cut some sandwiches to go with the coffee.

They were beginning to feel like old friends by this time, and Jill asked him his name.

"Oh, I'm sorry," he said. "I should have told you when I first came. I'm Gary Somers."

Jill gave a gasp of horror.

"Gary Somers?" she stammered. "From Strathclyde University?"

"That's right! But how did you know?"

How did she know? Jill felt weak at the knees. This was the boy her friend Stella Murray had met at a dance two or three weeks ago and had been head-over-heels about ever since. She had sung his praises to Jill day in, day out. There had never, in Stella's words, been a boy so dashing, handsome, clever and sports-loving. She had invited him home, and he had made an impression on all the family. She intended bringing him to the party to show him off to Jill, but he hadn't come, and Stella had brought another boy whose name Jill couldn't even remember.

Jill stood, trying to collect her thoughts. What exactly had she said to Gary about Stella? Something very unkind, she was sure. It served her right for being too impulsive and thoughtless. Her mother was always telling her to count ten before she made a remark about anyone.

Gary was looking at her rather curiously.

"How did you know about me?" he repeated.

Jill sought in vain for an answer, and after a moment Gary answered his own question for himself.

"Of course. It was Mrs Murray who gave me your mother's name for a demonstration; you're friends, aren't you?"

Jill nodded, still unable to trust herself to speak. Gary looked at her keenly as another thought struck him.

"So you know Stella Murray very well? In fact, she's your best friend, the girl you were speaking of a while ago?" His tone was grave.

"Oh, Gary." Jill's voice was full of apology. "I didn't know who you were, honestly, or I would never have said what I did. Please believe me!"

The young man turned his head away without answering.

"Please don't take any notice of what I said," Jill went on in a belated attempt to correct the impression she had given. "I was in a bad temper because of the rain and the clearing-up and everything."

"It's good of you to want to be loyal to your friend," Gary said at last, " but she did let you down, didn't she? And she hadn't said a word to me about a party either. That's strange."

" Oh, you know Stella, she's a bit of a scatterbrain, like me ; does things on impulse, and sometimes forgets really important matters," continued Jill, wondering if her words were making things better or worse.

" She didn't forget to bring another fellow along to the party," Gary added bitterly.

" Oh, there's probably quite a simple explanation for that." Jill was trying hard to undo any harm she had done.

She knew that Stella could usually talk her way out of any awkward situation.

THE washing-up demonstration was finished in a much quieter mood, both Jill and Gary busy with their own thoughts. Finally, Gary packed up the machine and took it out to his van again, leaving Jill with a pile of literature to hand to her mother.

" Well, cheerio !" he said. " See you again some time, I hope."

" Cheerio just now !"

Jill noted that it was still raining heavily as she went thoughtfully back into the house. Gary had seemed so depressed when he left, very different from the cheerful young man who had appeared at the back door earlier. She felt depressed, too. What was she going to do to get through this dull, wet day?

She wondered whether Stella would ever find out what had been said about her. Maybe it would be the end of the friendship between them. But meanwhile, why hadn't she come round as she usually did on a Saturday morning? It might be a good idea to telephone, thought Jill, in case she were ill.

Stella's voice when she answered the telephone was full of excitement.

" I can't stop a minute," she said. " Rory's waiting for me, he's got a marvellous sports car."

" Rory?" queried Jill.

" You know, I brought him to the party. He's great fun . . ." She poured it all out, and only when she stopped for breath could Jill get a word in.

" But, Stella, you said . . ."

" I did mean to help you, honestly I did ! I didn't know Rory would turn up this morning, and—well, you know how it is !"

" You're going out now with this new boy friend?" Jill inquired calmly, and if Stella caught something bitter in her voice she passed it off in her usual way.

" We're off to St Andrews. A friend of his has got a discotheque there. It'll be great fun. 'Bye now, must dash !"

" Wait, Stella !" Jill insisted, wanting to get something clear in her mind. " Didn't you tell me you were going to see a rugby match today with Gary Somers?"

" Did I say that?" Stella responded with a giggle. " Rugby in this weather ! I must have been mad. Oh, it's all right, I haven't really let him down. I phoned his mum and told her to tell Gary I'd a bad cold. Cheerio!"

JILL heard her bang down the receiver and she felt herself trembling. She supposed she shouldn't be surprised at the things Stella did. Sometimes the way she got herself out of scrapes was really amusing. But this time was different, this time Jill was really angry. She felt she had at last had enough of her friend's tiresome behaviour.

As she left the hall, there came another knock at the back door. It was Gary Somers again, looking more crestfallen than ever. He was full of apologies, wondering if he could use the telephone.

"I thought you were well away," Jill said with surprise. "What happened?"

"The van won't start. Either there's water in the carburettor or the battery's flat. I don't have much luck with this job, do I?"

The phoning finished, he still seemed to linger.

"I was wondering," Gary said at last. "I suppose you wouldn't be free this afternoon?

"I'll be honest with you," he added, "I was going to take Stella to a rugby match but she's got a cold. Maybe that's why she didn't come round to help you this morning."

He looked at Jill to see what she thought of this explanation, and she nodded her head as if she agreed, not knowing what to say. How dare Stella put her in this impossible position!

"The match'll be off with all this rain," Gary continued. "There's not an awful lot to do on a Saturday afternoon in Glenrogie, but I think there's a good film on or we could go to the ice rink if you prefer. Please don't think you're just a stop-gap, it was just that I thought we both needed cheering up a bit. But, of course, you may have something better to do."

Jill considered the invitation. She had already been wondering what to do with the rest of the day and she was beginning to have quite a liking for this young man. Otherwise, why should she feel so indignant at Stella's treatment of him?

"Do come!" Gary pleaded, looking so unhappy that Jill decided it was only reasonable to try and cheer him up a little.

"I'd love to go skating again," she said. "I haven't been for ages. What time shall I be ready?"

The noisy arrival of a breakdown truck was heard outside, so they hastily fixed details for the afternoon and Gary went off, looking more cheerful already.

I hope I don't live to regret this later, Jill thought as she set about preparing herself some lunch. She was still torn between the remnants of loyalty to Stella and anger at her devious ways. Having taken a liking for Gary was an added complication.

"Oh, what's the use of worrying?" she said to herself, beating up eggs for an omelette.

The visit to the ice rink was a great success. After some initial nervousness, due to being out of practice, Jill found she could do quite well. Gary, as she had expected, was quite expert, and she begged him to leave her to her own devices in a corner of the rink reserved for novices, while he went off on his own.

He evidently appreciated her thoughtfulness, and she watched him, fascinated, as he went through quite a complicated routine.

Presently, however, the loudspeakers began to play some well-known music, and Gary came back to Jill.

" Come and try this with me," he invited, holding out a hand to her.

" I'm not good enough," Jill answered. " I'm nowhere near your class !"

" Nonsense !" Gary replied. " It's just a question of practice."

" And good strong ankles," Jill added. " Mine are already beginning to protest."

" The music will go off soon . . . just keep moving. Come on !"

It certainly was easier than it looked. With one of Gary's strong arms round her shoulders and his hand in hers, Jill felt herself skimming over the ice.

" Breathe in naturally," Gary instructed. " In, out, in, out. That's fine, you're doing well !"

Such praise gave Jill a warm glow inside. She hadn't felt so happy for a long time, and wanted the music to go on and on, but after ten minutes or so Gary steered into the rail.

" That's enough for the first time," he said, gently releasing her but keeping one arm near until she fully regained her balance.

" The first time," Jill faltered.

" Yes, we'll have another go next week. You will come, won't you?" Jill remained silent, but Gary hardly seemed to notice.

" You've the makings of a first-class skater, just the partner I've been hoping for, and you're small and light, I bet I could lift you over my head like the champions do," he went on excitedly.

" Gary ! Stop ! You're going much too fast for me ! I haven't said yet I'll come again. Besides," Jill added with a pathetic little smile, " I'm tired, can I sit down?"

" I'm a selfish brute," Gary answered. " Can you make it to the tables over there, or shall I try out your weight and carry you?"

" Don't you dare !" retorted Jill, and started off, though holding the rail this time.

WHAT'll you have," Gary asked when they were seated, " coffee or cola ? "

" Oh, a long cold drink, please," Jill answered.

" Drink it slowly then," advised Gary in a fatherly way, and Jill hid a smile. It was very pleasant to have someone thinking about her welfare. What a thoroughly nice boy Gary was !

The thought brought Stella to her mind, and she felt there was a question she had to ask.

" Did you ever bring Stella skating?" she inquired.

Gary sat up with a start.

" Stella?" he said with astonishment. " Stella wouldn't come skating

15

—she would be much too afraid of making a fool of herself whilst learning. No, if Stella Murray couldn't do a thing perfectly she wouldn't do it at all."

It was true, of course, and Jill knew it.

"But I learned when I was small, about eight or nine."

"Ah, but you're different, Jill," Gary replied.

"You will come again, won't you?" he went on. "We get on so well together, and I don't only mean with the skating. I don't know quite how to put this, but I feel you wouldn't let a fellow down."

Jill felt confused. What was coming now?

"I wasn't going to tell you at first," went on Gary, "but now I feel I must. I want everything to be straight and honest between us. I saw Stella this morning!"

"You did? Where?"

"While I was trying to start the engine of the van. The sports car passed with that fellow driving and Stella sitting beside him. She knows I saw her, even though the hood was up. She looked right at me and giggled in that way she has. I guess I looked a mess, standing there in the rain trying to see what was wrong with the engine. She was supposed to have a bad cold and couldn't come out!"

Jill stretched out a consoling hand. She was very glad that Gary knew of Stella's latest deceitful behaviour, and very relieved that she herself hadn't had to tell him. Now she had nothing to reproach herself with.

Gary took her outstretched hand and gave it a little squeeze.

"Thanks, Jill," he said. "I'm well and truly over it!"

"I'll meet you here next Saturday if you like, Gary, and be your partner. Shall I?" Jill asked then.

"Yes, we'll be partners!"

There was a special meaning in his look as this time he took her hand and held it in a hard, tight grasp.

The thrill of the sledge is over, now it's time for tea.

Amanda's Lucky Panda

by Jean McDougall

EVERY year the papers said the same thing. This Christmas and New Year had been an all-time record spending spree, and Amanda Bailey just wished someone would tell her how it was done.

The end result, as far as she was concerned, was that there was usually far too much of January left to match the dwindling reserves in her purse.

In the bus she did a spot of mental budgeting, the food she would have to buy, to say nothing of fares and tights. She needed at least one session with the hairdresser, two if she could possibly stretch to it.

Her hair was very fine, inclined to fly away in the slightest breeze, or drop lankly around her oval face if not looked after. To give it body she really needed a perm, which was more expense, but luckily she still had the fiver Aunt Matilda had given her as a Christmas present.

The way things are going, she thought wryly, I may need to break into it to keep myself solvent till next pay day. At least she wouldn't starve, for her firm issued luncheon vouchers to all their employees and generously supplied morning and afternoon teas at nominal cost.

WHEN the bus reached Argyle Street, she normally changed for one that would drop her at Charing Cross. Sometimes if she was early or there wasn't a bus in sight, she would take the opportunity to nip into the supermarket at Inglis corner for a packet of biscuits or tea or whatever Lana, her flat-mate, asked her to bring home.

Lana, who worked at night in a discotheque, usually spent most of the mornings in bed, catching up with her sleep, but she more than pulled her weight with household shopping in the afternoons, and by the time Amanda got home from the office, there was generally something cooking.

Today, Lana had asked her to get some coffee and, since there was no sign of the second bus, she hurried into the shop, fumbling for money in her purse.

One of the smaller windows was still suffering from the Christmas shopping onslaught. Cheek by jowl with train sets were baby dolls and spinning tops, Monopoly and chemistry sets. On top of the higgledy-piggledy pile lay a panda, a huge fellow in black and white fur who was at least three feet long and had large black button eyes. The woebegone expression made her want to laugh, then she stopped to sympathise.

" Poor old fellow. Weren't you wanted, either ? "

" May I help you ? "

Behind her was a girl of her own age, with merry eyes that flashed between the customer and the windowful of toys.

" How much do you want for him ? " Amanda inquired, not really intending to buy him at that moment, but feeling something was expected of her for lingering so long in this part of the store.

" The panda ? " The girl smiled at her in delight. " Oh, I'm so pleased you're thinking of buying him. He's a pet, isn't he ? "

" Now, wait a minute. I'm not sure I want to buy the panda, I was just wondering how much it would cost."

The girl flicked the price ticket disappointedly.

" Oh, dear, I see they haven't got round to reducing this lot of toys yet, but I know they intend to. Look, could you manage to look in a little later, once I've seen my supervisor ? "

Amanda flicked over the ticket and whistled.

" Six pounds ! Goodness, they'd have to reduce it quite a bit before I could even consider buying. Thanks all the same."

The salesgirl nodded sympathetically.

" Everything's so dear nowadays. I'm paying the earth for a quarter share of a flat, and wondering just how long I can keep it up without going broke." She shrugged apologetically. " But here I am boring you with my troubles, and I expect you've plenty of your own. Can I get whatever it was you came in for ?"

Amanda grimaced.

" A small jar of instant coffee. I'm afraid it's quite a comedown after looking at a six-pound panda !"

" It may be made quite a bit cheaper," the girl told her eagerly, " and if you like to leave me your name, I'll keep him for you if you can tell me when you'll be back."

" Amanda Bailey, but if I don't show up by closing time tonight, just forget it."

" Panda and Amanda ! That's just perfect. If I'm not around when you come back ask for me. I'm Iris Martin. Meantime, I'll lay this aside till the price ticket's been altered."

" Don't let anyone ever tell you you're not a good salesgirl." Amanda smiled as she made for the door, clutching the coffee.

" See you later," Iris said confidently. " I'm sure you'll be back."

I'M sure I shan't, Amanda thought humorously as she reached the street again and had to run for the bus. In another ten minutes she'd be late for the office and Mr Harkness would be looking at the wall clock over his spectacles in silent reproof.

On occasion he could relax the stern expression and praise his staff when they put in an extra heavy day or dealt tactfully with some unusually difficult clients, and yesterday had been a case in point.

Amanda had decided to eat sandwiches in the office at lunch time instead of going out. Normally the office was closed to callers between one and two-thirty, but when people travelled up from the country to consult one or other of the partners, one had to stretch the rules a bit, particularly when they overlooked the precaution of writing or phoning first to make an appointment.

Tam Mallory had plainly no intention of being kept out, locked doors or no locked doors. He kept his thumb on the push bell till in exasperation Amanda put her cup back and got up to open the front door.

Although the notice stating hours of business was written in huge letters and numbers, old Mr Mallory hadn't spared it a glance.

" In my day," he growled, striding into the office without waiting for an invitation, " solicitors' offices were open from first thing in the morning."

" Does Mr Harkness expect you ? I'm afraid he's still at court, along with Mr Blackie."

" Where's young Matt Mathieson ? He was always here when I used to come a bit more regularly."

Amanda thought for a moment. Young Matt Mathieson ?

" There was a Mr Mathieson retired the week I started here, about three months ago."

Mr Mallory, a big, husky outdoors type, sank to a chair, shaking his head.

" Mathieson retired. Well, well ! Now, young lady, let me introduce myself and tell you exactly what I've come for."

19

The blue eyes that seemed more at home scanning distant horizons than focusing on the printed book regarded her keenly.

" I'm planning to sell one of my farms and I need some details which you can get me from the Title Deeds, and also the date of the original purchase by my father. You'll probably have that on file somewhere. And time is of the essence."

She hesitated.

" Mr Mallory, I hope you won't be offended, but how do I know you are who you say you are ? Mr Harkness wouldn't like it if . . ."

" When did Harkness ever like anything ?" He waved him aside, but nodded approvingly at the girl. " Yes, you're right, I ought to provide proof of my identity. Well, will this do ?"

He tossed a bankbook towards her and a cheque book with his name printed on each page.

" That suit you, Miss Sherlock Homes ?"

" Thank you." She returned the books to the twinkling-eyed farmer. " May I offer you a cup of tea, Mr Mallory ? I'm afraid I'll still have to phone Mr Harkness for permission to dig into the private files. You understand, don't you ?"

" Of course, lass. I'm not here to make trouble for you and I'll accept your kind offer of tea, for I'm fair parched."

He also accepted one of the pancakes which was part of her lunch.

" Is this all you eat in the middle of the day ? No wonder you're as thin as a wand, young lady."

SHE left him with the office newspaper to read while she went next door to try to locate one of the partners at the courts. Finally Mr Harkness came on the line, a little annoyed at being disturbed.

" Oh, Tam Mallory ? Trust him to come breezing in without bothering to make an appointment ! Yes, all right, Amanda. Look out his file, but don't let him walk off with any of the papers. Information's all right, but anything else we'll send on to him when I get back."

Most of her lunch hour went on typing out data for Mr Mallory from the thick file kept in the partners' private office. He thanked her with quiet sincerity.

" You're a smart girl, almost as good as young Mathieson. Thank you, my lass, and tell that employer of yours to give you some time off to make up for the extra you've spent on me."

" It was a pleasure." She gave him a warm smile. " I hope you have everything you need in this envelope, but if not, please telephone. Mr Harkness says he'll be glad to post on anything else you need."

" Like five thousand pounds, maybe ?" the old man queried, his eyes dancing.

" Anything else apart from that maybe," she replied, seeing him to the outside door. Two of her fellow typists were returning from lunch, and Mr Mallory jerked his head in their direction.

" How many girls does Harkness employ now ?"

" Five of us."

" Things must be looking up for the firm. Well, Miss Amanda, thanks again for your help. It's nice to have something done so ungrudgingly and so pleasantly."

When Mr Harkness returned she was enthusing about " such a charming old man."

For once his professional reserve dropped from him.

" That's what you think. If he's crossed, he can be a very tough old man."

" Can't we all when we're crossed ?"

But Mr Harkness had pulled around him his cloak of reserve again and was dictating letters in reply to the day's mail.

T HIS morning he wasn't at his usual desk when she entered, but the other girls were, and good mornings flew back and forth for a bit.

Underneath, she thought she sensed an air of excitement, but put it down to someone's exciting date the previous evening.

Then Tina leaned across.

" Guess who's in the private room just now," she whispered.

" I've no idea," Amanda replied.

The People's Friend Annual

" Ed Mallory, and wait till you see him. He's the handsomest . . ."

" Mr Mallory's son ? Well, I can believe he'll be handsome if he's anything like his dad."

" Lucky you !"

" Me ?" Amanda laughed disbelievingly. " How come ?"

" Well, you obviously took a trick with his father. That gives you a head start over the rest of us."

" I'm not the country type," she protested. " What possible interests could we have in common ?"

She shook her head, smiling at her romantic friend. It was the same when any presentable young man entered the office. Sometimes Amanda wondered how they would all react if the partners ever took a young and attractive man into the business. The competition amongst the five would be terrific ; amongst the four, she corrected herself humorously. Ed Mallory, or anyone else for that matter, could count her out.

MR BLACKIE sent for her fifteen minutes later.
" Oh, this is Mr Mallory, Amanda. Mr Mallory, this is . . ."
" The young lady who was so helpful to my father yesterday."

He had the same far-seeing blue eyes, and the rugged complexion of someone constantly in the open air. Amanda was beginning to feel uncomfortable before the smiling scrutiny when Mr Blackie began dictating a contract for the purchaser and seller of one of the Mallory farms.

Every now and then he paused in the course of dictating to consult with the younger man on various points, but eventually he concluded, looking apologetically at his watch.

" Now, Amanda, I wonder if we could impose on you to work right on till you've finished typing this ? Mr Mallory's catching the three o'clock train back and I'd like him to have the contract with him."

" That's all right," she said readily. " It'll be no trouble."

" Perhaps we could have lunch together when you're through," Ed Mallory suggested easily.

" Really, there's no need . . ."

Mr Blackie cut in.

" You young people sort yourselves out after the work's done, not before. Now, I'll have to leave you to it, Amanda. Are there any queries before I go ?"

She shook her head, gathering book and pen together along with some papers and, with a smiling nod to both men, she returned to her desk.

" Well, what happened ?" one of her friends asked. " We thought you and Ed Mallory had eloped or something."

" Don't be daft."

There was no chance to say more, for both Mr Blackie and his partner were at her desk.

" It might be as well," Mr Blackie told her, " if you take a taxi down to the courts later and let me look it over. You can give young Mallory a lift while you're at it, and then . . ." His eyes twinkled. " If the pair of you want to have lunch, that'll be quite all right, Amanda.

22

And by the way, share out the work with the others and hand this out as well. It's a gift from Mr Mallory, senior, to all of you."

Amanda opened the envelope and stared hard at the fifteen crisp notes inside. There were varied reactions from the other four when she laid them on the desk and from a doorway behind them they heard Ed Mallory's voice.

"Hope you're not going to hold it against me. It was entirely my father's idea."

"It's crazy," Amanda said when she got her breath back. "Anything I did for him yesterday I was well paid to do by the firm, and also by the kind way he thanked me for my trouble."

"Well, he meant it kindly enough," Ed justified his father. "And I hope you'll all accept it in the spirit it was sent."

"Here." Amanda thrust the envelope into Tina's hands. "You look after dividing it out, will you? I'll simply have to get on with the typing."

The others were more than willing to do any copy work for her and Ed Mallory made himself useful by making them all cups of coffee and even washing up the used cups under the tap.

AT length the work was finished and checked. All that now remained was to take a taxi to where Mr Blackie would be, let him look it over, and after that things could be allowed to simmer down.

One of the others phoned for a taxi and minutes later, Amanda and Ed Mallory were seated inside, being whisked towards the city centre.

"I was worried for a bit," he admitted, "when I saw your face after you'd opened Dad's envelope. You looked sort of offended."

"I was surprised, taken aback, but I'd never be offended over anything your father did or said. We'll all be writing to thank him and let him know what we've bought with his generous gift."

The taxi had drawn up at their destination and there was no opportunity for further conversation while she settled up with the driver on the firm's behalf, then raced into the large building in search of Mr Blackie, leaving Ed at the entrance.

Ten minutes later she was back.

"Tired of waiting?"

He shook his head.

"Not me. I've been enjoying the chance to study the passing throng." With a grin he indicated a poor-looking man on the opposite side of the street who was trying to sell blades to passers-by.

"Where would you like to lunch?"

"Oh, I don't mind." He shrugged. "Any place you choose will suit me fine."

She took him into the restaurant of a large store nearby, thinking what a pity it was that, when he was so like his father in many ways, he had somehow failed to obtain much of the old man's charm of manner.

He didn't waste much time trying to impress or charm the waitress, but concentrated all his efforts on building up a good picture of himself in Amanda's eyes.

" I could catch a later train," he was suggesting, " if you happen to be free this evening."

Amanda gasped inwardly, thinking of the five girls, herself included, all pounding away at their typewriters in order to get the agreement typed up to allow him to be on the three o'clock train home.

" Your father will be expecting you at tea-time."

" I could telephone, but it wouldn't matter, really. He expects me when he sees me."

" Well, I'm not free," she said, starting on her soup and thinking of Iris Martin who would be hoping to make a sale this evening before five-thirty.

" Boy friend ?"

" No. Panda friend, actually."

She smiled at his astonishment, then went on to explain about this morning.

" And so I'll be able to buy him now, thanks to your father's generosity."

" Do you mind telling me," he asked heavily, " who you want the toy for ?"

" For me. Do you think that's being silly ?"

" Oh, no, of course not."

But plainly he did, and she had to suppress a smile. There was no point in trying to explain just why she wanted to buy the panda. He would never have understood in a month of Sundays and for the rest of the meal they stayed on safe topics like books they'd read and films they'd seen and television programmes they liked to watch.

OUTSIDE the station he shook hands with her, holding it a little longer than necessary while she stood awkwardly, wanting to pull it away, yet not wishing to offend.

" I could come back to town whenever you say, Amanda. I'd like nothing better than to see you again."

" Well, I expect I'll be in the office any day you happen to be visiting."

" I meant some time you're on holiday, or you could come to the farm. I'm sure you'd enjoy it there."

She shook her head.

" Not really, Ed, but thanks for asking. I'm afraid I'm the city type who loves the bright lights and loud music. I'd be pretty lost amongst all those animals, and the peace and quiet would drive me round the bend."

He shrugged, moving his hand in a gesture of resignation.

" Well, if that's the way it is."

" Yes, I'm afraid so, but thanks for the lunch today. I did enjoy it."

When she got back to the office the girls were all agog to learn how she had got on. Only Tina refrained from questioning her and she guessed it was because she was more than a little keen on Ed Mallory herself.

" Not my type at all," Amanda whispered to her, " though he's a very nice chap. Next time, I hope you'll be the one he takes to lunch."

Tina looked scared yet pleased.

" Do you think it would be all right for me to write Mr Mallory thanking him for the tip ?"

" But of course you must, and the sooner the better."

THERE was a hold-up of traffic at five that evening, and Amanda thought for a while she wasn't going to be able to reach Iris in time to take the panda home. In the end, she was lucky to hail a taxi which took her over the approach roads to the new bridge and round by Bothwell Street to the corner of Argyle and Oswald Streets and the shop where Iris worked.

" Well, you made it," the dark-haired girl greeted her warmly, as though they were old friends, but it seemed to Amanda she was not looking quite so chirpy as she had been in the morning. In fact, now she was closer, she felt sure the other girl had been crying.

" Tough day ?" she asked sympathetically.

" In a way. It probably serves me right," Iris said frankly. " Earlier today I was grumbling about all the money I was having to pay for my share of the flat. Well, I heard at lunch time our landlord has given us notice to quit. The building's scheduled for demolition, apparently."

" Oh, no. That's terrible."

" Well, never mind my tale of woe. Here's your panda. They're letting it go for half-price, if you still want it. Three pounds, and a bargain at the price."

Amanda handed over her share of Mr Mallory's gift, feeling a tremendous thrill as she lifted the big panda into her arms.

" Wrap it for you ?"

" No, thanks. I'll carry it like this, though I just wonder if they'll let me on a bus, especially if they're busy."

" If a lift out the south-west direction would help, my brother comes round for me in exactly five minutes. He can't park on this street, of course, so it's a case of being on the pavement ready to step in the moment he draws up."

" Won't he mind ?"

" Not Rex."

" Well, in that case, thank you. I could get a bus at the Toll that would take me out to the Shields."

Iris had asked Amanda to wait on the opposite side of Oswald Street as her brother usually took that lane when turning out of Argyle Street.

The red car pulled up almost beside her, but the driver was naturally on the lookout for Iris and kept glancing anxiously across the street.

Once he glanced in Amanda's direction, giving her a faint smile as she nursed the panda. Then when he spotted his sister dodging the traffic as she crossed over, he leaned over to open the car door.

" Come on, Amanda," Iris called, pulling at the handle of the back door. " Hop in. Time for introductions later."

" Now where do you want to go ?"

" Iris says you go past Paisley Road Toll," Amanda answered. " Well, if you could drop me off there, I can easily get a bus going past where I stay."

" Talking of places to stay," Iris remarked gloomily from the front seat. " I've got the sack today."

" From the shop ? Hard lines, Iris."

" No, from my landlord."

YOU don't stay together then ?" Amanda asked, hugging the panda. " No, Rex has digs in Cardonald. The flat we had is at Halfway."

" I don't know if you'd be interested in moving in with Lana and me, Iris," Amanda said slowly. " Of course, we'd have to see Lana first."

" Do you really mean it, that there might be a place for me in your flat ? Goodness, that would certainly solve my problems, provided the rent's not sky high."

" It's only a nominal rent actually. The house belonged to Lana's grandmother and we managed to get the tenancy when she died. Let's arrange an evening this week for you to come and look at the place and meet Lana, and we can take it from there."

" How about gate-crashers ?" Rex inquired. " Any allowed ?"

" None," his sister answered, shaking a firm head. " Positively none."

" We might make an exception in your case." Amanda laughed.

" Done." He nodded his head vigorously. " Seems to me that's a lucky panda you have in the back there."

Amanda sat back against the upholstery with the panda on her knee. It was funny she had never thought to link it up with good fortune, but Rex was right.

When the car turned left at the Toll, she knew Rex intended delivering her safely at her own front door before driving on to his own home and his sister's flat. Such a lot had happened today it had left her both tired and exhilarated at one and the same time, but the prevailing feeling was one of happiness, of the bliss that comes from meeting a kindred spirit. Maybe the luck was not bound up with the panda so much as with Rex Martin himself.

A walk with the dog in desolate February.

by
Nan
Baxter

THE grandfather clock in the lobby struck four and Mrs Boswell opened the front door to listen. Sure enough, the high-pitched cries of children came to her clearly. Kinthorpe School was empty- ing for another day and among that excited throng was her grandson, Tommy.

At one time the sound of those voices had been like music in her ears. She had waited expectantly to see Tommy rounding the corner into Creevie Road, and come rushing up the steps to Eden Cottage, calling out to her. At such moments Granny Boswell's heart had been filled with pride and happiness.

But three months ago that had stopped and now Tommy would be heading the other way, down the Back Road to home. Which was as it should be, Mrs Boswell knew. Yet the acceptance did nothing to lessen her loneliness or banish that cold, empty feeling of being shut out from her own family circle.

She sat down by the window of her sitting-room that overlooked the

Four Makes A Family

village. Here, among the Perthshire hills, the pattern of her life had unfolded. There was nothing extraordinary about it. She had married Donald, the boy next door, then Peter had been born. The years had passed, and it was Peter's turn to marry and he had chosen Mary, a girl from the neighbouring village. When her grandson had arrived, Mrs Boswell's happiness had been complete.

She remembered now all the joy of Tommy's early days; the delight of cradling him in her arms, pushing the pram, watching him crawl, then listening to his first words. Mary had been eager that Tommy's grandmother should share in his gradual development, and it was a privilege that Mrs Boswell both appreciated and respected.

Strange how suddenly all that happiness had turned to sadness when Mary was rushed to hospital and never recovered from the operation.

Peter and she had clung to each other that evening, Mrs Boswell recalled. Through their tears they had looked down at Tommy, asleep and unaware of the tragedy that surrounded him.

But life had to go on. Somehow, Mrs Boswell and her son would manage. Peter was an agent for feeding stuffs, travelling round the farms, but he could make breakfast and see Tommy off to school. At lunch time the boy would go to his granny's and when school was over he would return there for tea.

Then they would wander down the Back Road together and there would be a meal and a welcome for Peter's homecoming. A big adjustment in the lives of them all, and one that necessitated a coming and going between the two houses. But it was better that way, they decided, and they had faith that it would work out.

A ND so, for Granny Boswell there emerged from her grief a mission of caring that helped to lighten her own sense of loss and to give Tommy and his father some of that love and understanding they so desperately needed.

Tommy was a bewildered, frightened child, breaking his heart at times over the loss of his mother. Eagerly, he would turn to his granny for comfort. A bonny bairn, with his dark hair and those brown eyes that made Mrs Boswell think of the deep pools in the burn.

And he was quiet, finding difficulty in making friends. One never knew what lay behind those silences or the sudden bounds into his grandmother's arms as if the hurt was too much for him to bear.

But gradually Granny Boswell gained the boy's confidence. Watching Tommy's growth was like seeing a sapling develop and spread its branches. He gained courage and a new independence. Sometimes he would come to Eden Cottage, a little ashamed of his bruises, but triumphant that he had come out best in a fight.

And Mrs Boswell would understand and be glad. She was seventy now, but she helped Tommy to dig for worms for the fishing and gave him a white rabbit for his birthday. The love between a granny and her grandson can grow very deep.

Peter was happier, too. As the months progressed his eyes lost that sunken look. He began to join his friends at the bowling green and to go to Perth for curling. But with it all he was still lonely. The memory of Mary came to him so often and, without the comfort of his mother and his beloved son, life would have been intolerable.

Yet after every winter comes the spring and with it a new promise. Peter Boswell was still a young man. He was just over thirty and Mary had been dead for almost three years when he first saw Sarah Turnbull.

She was walking across the fields to her father's farm, her fair hair blowing in the breeze, a Labrador at her heels. Different, somehow, from any girl Peter had ever seen and his interest was aroused. He made it his business to visit her father fairly frequently for orders so that he could have an opportunity of speaking to her.

" I wonder," Peter said one evening after supper, " do you think you could stay on longer tonight? I'd like to go out and I may be late. I can't leave Tommy alone."

Mrs Boswell looked at her son and sensed his excitement. There had been a sparkle in Peter's eyes recently that had pleased her and set her wondering.

" Who's the girl?" she asked boldly.

" I didn't think you'd guess," he replied smiling, and told his mother about Sarah Turnbull. " She's quiet and understanding. I've told her everything, about Mary and Tommy and you."

" And you're in love with each other?"

" Yes, we're in love." Peter was holding his mother's gaze, and it was a moment that seemed taken out of time.

" It's different from what went before." Peter was choosing his words carefully. " And so very wonderful. More mature, yet just as true and steadfast as it ever was. Love can be all-encircling. You'll like Sarah, Mother, and I hope that Tommy will, too."

Just for a second, his voice trembled.

" Bless you, my son." Mrs Boswell could say no more. To see Peter entering into a new fulfilment was her greatest wish, but she was thinking, too, of all the implications that this forthcoming marriage would bring.

She thought of Tommy and sighed. To a sensitive boy of eight, this change must inevitably bring difficulties. As for herself, she must learn to slip into second place, and that, too, wasn't going to be easy.

O NE summer afternoon, Peter brought Sarah Turnbull to Kinthorpe so that she could meet his mother and Tommy. Tall and elegant, she came into the room keeping close to Peter's side, smiling nervously, with her deep blue eyes full of concern. What an ordeal this must be for the girl, Mrs Boswell realised, and she went quickly forward and took Sarah in her arms.

" You're welcome, my dear." It was a tense moment, as they both searched for the understanding that they both needed. Soon their lives would be entwined, their love centred on that same man and his little son. They could only smile and hope that they could share a mutual happiness.

Then Sarah was turning to Tommy. Weeks ago, his father had told him what was about to happen. Now, Sarah was holding out her hand and

Tommy was taking it. Instinctively, Sarah knew better than make a fuss of him.

They all sat down and there was a sudden silence. Tommy was staring at Sarah with an intensity that made her move uneasily. She was being judged and the verdict, Sarah was certain, was extremely unfavourable.

The afternoon was not a success. Conversation dried up every few minutes, and it was a relief when Peter took Sarah away. That they were very much in love with each other was evident but Mrs Boswell sighed and wondered, and prayed.

Peter and Sarah were married quietly a month later. Tommy and his grandmother were in the front pew of the church and nothing escaped them. The boy crept closer and closer to his granny, and at the reception he never left her side. There were kisses and a flurry of confetti and the newly-married couple were off. Tommy and Mrs Boswell waved as if in a dream. Everything seemed so very unreal.

And then, for a whole fortnight, they were together in Eden Cottage. It was selfish, Granny Boswell knew, to be so delighted to have Tommy all to herself, and it was tempting to smother him in love. But it was her duty to prepare him for the homecoming of his new mother.

" But I don't want her in my home," Tommy declared defiantly.

" Your father does." How difficult it was to explain such matters to a child. " He needs someone to love and to love you, to make a happy home together. When you're a man you'll understand."

Tommy was staring at her in amazement.

" I remember my mum, my real mum." It was the first time the boy had mentioned his mother's name, and Granny Boswell saw that Tommy's eyes were filling with tears. " She was warm and cuddly, and she tucked me in at nights. I don't need anyone to do that now."

How well she understood Tommy's misgivings, but there was only one thing to say.

" It's going to be different, Tommy, and perhaps at first you won't like it. But your new mum is nice and she wants to care for you. Remember it's going to be difficult for her, too. I love her already, so won't you try and love her, too?"

Tommy nodded his head, but he didn't look very convinced.

THEY were both waiting for Peter and Sarah when they came back from their honeymoon. Sarah was the first to kiss Mrs Boswell, then Peter followed. Tommy was waiting and his father had him in his arms, hugging him tight.

" Did you miss me, son?"

" Yes, Dad."

But Tommy was looking beyond his father to this new mother of his who was coming nearer. She had nice blue eyes, but his own mum's had been brown. She was kissing him and he didn't like it, drawing back from her so that she was aware of his resentment. He just couldn't help it. He was so mixed up he didn't know what to say or do.

" Granny made a fish pie for your supper," he declared, and suddenly they were smiling and relaxed.

Four Makes A Family

But not for long. The same tension was there and Granny Boswell was almost glad when it was time to return to Eden Cottage. Peter and Sarah wandered up the Back Road with her, but Tommy had mysteriously disappeared.

BACK home, the young married couple faced up to the realities that lay ahead.

"It's going to be difficult, Peter." Sarah was in his arms, young and inexperienced, desperately anxious to do her best. "I'm an intruder in Tommy's eyes, and yet somehow I've got to capture his affection."

They had always talked frankly, but Sarah's voice was trembling now. "The memory of his mother is still with Tommy, and nothing must harm that. And there's Granny Boswell whom he loves so much, I don't want her to be hurt."

Peter was holding her tight.

"Together we'll win through," he said, hopefully. Wife, son, mother! He loved them all. Pray God that they would all find happiness together. But the miracle wouldn't happen in a day, he knew.

And he was right. At first Tommy was sullen and quiet, but Sarah had a little touch of magic that could coax a smile and create a quickening of interest.

Tommy tried hard to resist it, but gradually he was being captured by Sarah's charm. Yet there was still a long way to go, they both knew, before he would come to accept her completely.

Granny Boswell watched as the family unit strengthened. They didn't forget her. She was there as an anchor of the old life and she had her place in the new.

The whole tempo of her life had changed. She didn't see Tommy so often, although the bond between them was still strong. And she hadn't come as close to Sarah as she had hoped. She loved the girl and she was sure Sarah felt the same, yet no matter how kind and considerate Sarah was, there was no denying the fact

A FAMILY OCCASION

*I*T was Christmas afternoon and young Dr Allison was hurrying along the hospital corridor.

"Emergency?" enquired a colleague.

"No. I'm rushing off home."

Just then sleet lashed the window behind them.

"What! In this weather!" his friend exclaimed, knowing Dr Allison's home was forty miles away.

"Yes, it's a family tradition always to be home for Christmas."

Through wind and sleet, along roads covered with slush, the doctor drove to keep a family tryst in the old familiar home.

"A Merry Christmas." His parents and sisters welcomed him warmly, glad to see him safe. Presents were exchanged and they settled down to hear all the family news in the firelight.

It was a family Christmas . . . a lovely echo of Bethlehem and the child in the manger.

That, too, was a family occasion.

Rev. T. R. S. Campbell

that Granny Boswell was suddenly an outsider. Sometimes bitterness enveloped her, and then with a quickened conscience she would rebuke herself for being unfair.

Now, as she continued to sit by the window, Mrs Boswell shivered in her loneliness. Often, nowadays, she felt lazy. There seemed so little object in life. She had to force herself, as she was doing now, even to get up and make a cup of tea.

And then standing there she was suddenly alert, listening and holding her breath. It couldn't be! She must be dreaming. But there was no doubting the familiar sound of those footsteps. Tommy never came here now direct from school, but he was coming today.

He was in with a rush and it was like old times to see the sparkle in his eyes and his obvious eagerness to tell her some news.

" What do you think, Gran? We're going to have a school camp."

" That's something new." Mrs Boswell was sitting down and the boy was by her side. " Tell me all about it."

Tommy's words came tumbling out. All about the hut in the hills, miles away and up some track where they would spend a couple of nights. They would climb a mountain, fish in a loch and cook their own meals. Two of the teachers would be going with them.

" It's what they call an adventure," finished Tommy. " We've each to take just one blanket."

He was wildly excited about it all. How wonderful, reflected Mrs Boswell, to be so young and to thrill to a challenge like this.

" You'll enjoy yourself," she said. " I'll give you a packet of sweets to take with you. What does your mum say about it all?"

Tommy was looking at her dubiously.

" She doesn't know." His head was suddenly defiantly high. " We're supposed to ask for permission. Won't it do if I tell the teacher that you said it would be all right?"

" No, my boy."

HER words were firm, but Tommy was going on unheeding, and there was a yearning look on his face.

" Gran, I wish I could come back and stay with you."

It was a moment of triumph and temptation. Mrs Boswell's heart was beating madly and she wanted to pull Tommy into her arms and give him the assurance he desired.

" Mum's nice, but she's different." Tommy's eyes were wide and appealing. " I love you, Gran. Won't you let me come? I would be good and go your messages and help in the garden and . . ."

To have him to herself once more, to feel the warmth and energy of that young life surrounding her! Mrs Boswell was visualising it and smiling. Could anything be more tempting? But she knew it was impossible and there was only one answer.

" I would dearly like to have you here, laddie, but you see, it wouldn't be right. It's your mum's job to look after you, and she's doing it well, better than I could. I'm old and she's young."

She was trembling a little, but still resolute.

" And she loves you, Tommy, just as much as I do, even if it's in a different way. You've got to trust her."

Mrs Boswell was standing up.

" We must go to your mum now because she'll be wondering where you are. Tell her all about the camp and I know she'll be delighted. When the time comes she'll help you to pack your kit."

TOMMY'S hand was in hers as they went down the Back Road. They had reached the garden gate when Sarah came rushing out, scared-looking and pale.

" I've been up and down the road half a dozen times." She sighed thankfully. " I was afraid there might have been an accident. I never thought . . ."

She was looking at Granny Boswell inquiringly.

" I'm glad he was with you."

Then Tommy was telling his story all over again. They moved into the house and Sarah drew Tommy on to her knee.

" Of course you'll go to the camp. It will be the greatest fun. When you come back from all those adventures you'll almost be a man."

" Davie Smith thinks he'll cry when it gets dark."

" Would you like if I packed your little red engine, the one you take to bed with you every night? All the boys, I'm sure, will have something."

" Oh, thank you, Mum."

Mum! She was accepted at last. The miracle was happening and they were nearer to each other at that moment than they had ever been.

" And I shouldn't have gone to tell Granny first about the camp. She told me that and brought me home. But I still love my Granny."

" And so do I, more than ever," added Sarah.

But Mrs Boswell had slipped out of the house and Sarah saw from the window the solitary figure heading up the Back Road, to loneliness and the feeling that she wasn't needed any more. And Sarah's heart was full of compassion and understanding.

" Tommy," she said, " run after your Gran. Tell her that I want her here, back home."

She watched him, running eagerly. He would be a little breathless as he gave his grandmother the message. And then Mrs Boswell was turning, coming back to take her full and proper place in the family.

There would be a new purpose in life now for them all. A blackbird singing on the branch of a tree seemed to capture this new-found joy.

Sarah, her arms wide open, was going forward to welcome Granny Boswell. And with a little sob that was full of love Mrs Boswell was being enveloped in Sarah's embrace. Exhilaration swept over them.

Tommy, puzzled a little, was thinking of the forthcoming camp. Perhaps he would catch a fish, perhaps he would be the first to reach the top of the mountain. He would try hard. What a lot he would have to tell when he got home! And today, home had suddenly become a warmer, easier place.

It would be fun going away. But it would be fine to come back to Dad and Mum and Gran. And to all their love.

by
*Molly
Gair*

ONCE UPON A TIME...

LUCY BOYD saw the notice on her way home from work. It was already dark when she got off the bus, and the biting east wind made her shiver in spite of her warm tweed coat with its cosy, high collar.

It's the fireside for me tonight, she thought, hurrying along past the shops in the High Street.

There were still lights on in the windows and Stanton & Turner, the estate agents, was one. That's how Lucy saw the notice. Her eyes caught the words, "This Desirable Residence" and she stopped to read the description of Miss Neilson's house.

The property was to be sold by auction, but the contents of the house would be offered for sale on the afternoon before, at prices marked on each item. This was in accordance with the late owner's wishes.

How like Miss Neilson to let people buy some of her treasures at prices they could afford ! Lucy was remembering that frail, old-fashioned lady who had been such a good friend to her, and whose death last month left a blank in her life.

Lucy was on her way home from school that first time she encountered Miss Neilson. Thirteen years old, with long, fair hair and dreamy, blue eyes, she was sauntering along on a summer afternoon deeply engrossed in a story which her imaginative mind had conjured up. A story in which she, the heroine, led a very exciting life and met all kinds of strange people. So she wasn't really surprised when a small, white-haired lady called her as she was passing a gate in a high privet hedge.

" Child !" The high, clear voice had a commanding ring. " Come here, I want you."

Lucy stopped by the gate and looked along the path. Standing at the door of a neat, red sandstone villa was a figure dressed in black. In one hand she held a long envelope, and in the other an ebony cane which she tapped impatiently on the step.

Obediently, Lucy opened the gate and walked up the path. Miss Neilson's small, pointed face was stern, but the child wasn't afraid of her.

" Yes ? What can I do for you ?" she asked politely.

Miss Neilson held out the envelope.

" Are you going straight home ?" she asked.

Lucy nodded.

" Then will you drop this into the first pillar-box you come to ?"

Lucy took the bulky envelope. Was she being entrusted with important documents, she wondered. And would the act of dropping this envelope into the pillar-box start off a chain of exciting events, in the way of all good stories ?

" Is that all you want me to do ?" she asked Miss Neilson and the old lady's face broke into a smile.

" Tell me your name, child," she said, kindly.

" I'm Lucinda Mary Boyd," Lucy replied, because in the stories she wove about herself she always used her full name.

" That's a lovely name." Miss Neilson repeated it. " Come and see me again tomorrow. I'll have another letter for you to post."

THAT was the beginning of a friendship between a lonely, retired schoolmistress and a shy, imaginative girl, which ended when Miss Neilson died suddenly a few days after Lucy's nineteenth birthday.

The day of the sale at Miss Neilson's house was bright and sunny and the place was crowded when Lucy got there. It was early closing and everyone in the town seemed to be in the red sandstone villa. Lucy, small and determined, wormed her way inside where she hardly recognised the familiar drawing-room. Big furniture from other rooms lined the walls, and small items were laid out on tables placed in the bay windows. Lucy recognised many of the things there, small pieces of jewellery and trinkets which her old friend had worn, and ornaments which Lucy herself had often helped to dust. She must have something for a keepsake, but what should it be ?

And then she saw the Japanese fan made of cream silk on sticks of ivory. Lucy picked it up and, with a flick of her wrist, opened it so that she could see once again the pretty, hand-painted design of flowers and leaves. Miss Neilson had said it was very old when she'd explained to the young Lucy how the ladies of bygone days used their fans to encourage, or discourage, the young men who wished to court them.

" Have you decided on the fan ?" asked a voice at her elbow. " The price is on the ticket."

" Yes." Lucy nodded. " That's all I want."

But before she could hand over the money, a man on the other side of the table put in his bid.

" I'll pay double the price."

Lucy's blue eyes flashed angrily as she looked across at the tall, dark-haired speaker. So Roy Stewart was back in town, throwing his weight about as usual !

" I'm sorry, sir," the assistant said, taking Lucy's money and writing out a receipt. " We can't do that. Perhaps you'd like to choose something else ? "

But the fan was the only thing Roy wanted, and now Lucy Boyd was walking away with it.

Pushing his way through the crowd, he followed her out of the house.

" Lucy !" he called, striding down the garden path. " Lucy, let me explain . . ."

B UT Lucy didn't want to hear any explanations from Roy Stewart. Seeing a gap in the traffic she skipped smartly across the road and before he had a chance to catch up with her the traffic began to flow again and Roy was left on the pavement edge. He turned and walked slowly back to where he'd parked his car. He was disappointed about not getting the fan, and he knew his mother would be, too, when he told her about it.

But Mrs Stewart surprised him.

" Don't worry," she said. " It's not lost if Lucy Boyd's got it. Perhaps I can persuade her to lend it to me."

" I can't see the haughty Miss Boyd being so obliging," Roy murmured. " I wanted you to have that fan for your collection, and I'm furious with myself for not having seen it before she did."

Mrs Stewart smiled at her handsome son, but there was a puzzled expression on her own comely face.

" I don't know why Lucy Boyd has such a bad effect on you," she said. " You used to be such good friends."

" That was a long time ago." Roy scowled.

" Well, dear, if you're going to spend more time at home now you've got your promotion," his mother went on, " you'll be seeing quite a lot of Lucy. I've got plans to put on a Fashion Show during the town's Shopping Week next month. It will be a good opportunity to show my collection and I'm sure people will be interested in the styles of long ago."

Mrs Stewart was a dressmaker, and she had acquired a number of eighteenth and nineteenth century costumes with their accessories, of which she was rightly proud.

" I've got several ladies who'll be willing to wear the clothes," Mrs Stewart explained. " But, of course, they'll have to have the appropriate hair styles and this is where Lucy can help me. Being a hairdresser she'll know just what to do."

Roy groaned. His job as a surveyor had taken him all over Britain during the past three years but now, at twenty-five, he had an appointment with the local council and would be permanently at home.

" Oh, well," he said, " you can tell me when the house is likely to be full of women in crinolines and bustles, and I'll arrange to be out on those nights."

NOT far away, in a red brick house in Rosevale Gardens, Lucy was in her bedroom examining Miss Neilson's fan. Closed, and dangling from her wrist on its thin, silk cord, it was light and slender, hardly more than the thickness of a school ruler. But when she opened it there was a semi-circle of shimmering silk with a painted floral design in pink and green and gold, the colours still bright and clear. As she moved it slowly to and fro, fanning the air, Lucy's eyes grew dreamy.

Who, she wondered, had been the owner of this lovely thing before Miss Neilson acquired it ? Had it belonged to some gay, eighteenth century belle of the ball ? Or had the girl been a shy person like herself, glad to use the open fan to hide her nervous blushes ? And now that Lucy had it, what was she going to do with it ?

With a sigh she closed the fan and lifted the lid of a square, japanned box lying beside her on the bed. This was where she kept her treasures, and this was where the fan would lie, wrapped in tissue paper, among odds and ends of souvenirs and photographs.

I'll have to turn out this box, Lucy thought. There's not enough room in it for everything. I must stick these photographs in an album.

She tipped the box upside down and began to rearrange the contents, putting the photographs in a pile beside her. As she lifted each one, she looked at it ; at some she smiled, while others made her laugh out loud.

There was one photograph Lucy looked at for a long time, which had been taken in Miss Neilson's garden by the old lady. Roy Stewart, a tall, pleasant-looking lad of nineteen was smiling down at Lucy, small and child-like in her school uniform. It was in the early days of her friendship with Miss Neilson and she'd taken Roy, whom she'd known all her life, to meet her new friend.

What a pity people change, Lucy thought bitterly. In those days she'd loved Roy Stewart. His mother and hers were old friends and Roy, having no sisters, treated Lucy with gentle affection. But when she left school and started training to be a hairdresser, his attitude towards her changed to one of patronage whenever they met. Fortunately their paths didn't cross very often. In fact, for the last three years she'd hardly seen him at all, and to encounter him at the sale had been an unpleasant surprise.

She laid the fan gently in the box and closed the lid. It was the only thing she could do, but she thought it a pity such a pretty thing should be shut away like that.

BUT Miss Neilson's fan wasn't destined to stay long in Lucy Boyd's souvenir box.
    Having decided to show her collection of gowns, Mrs Stewart set about organising the programme with an enthusiasm which soon infected the people she invited to act as models. Lucy Boyd was one of them.

At first, when Mrs Stewart suggested Lucy would be the ideal person to wear a lovely, nineteenth century ball dress, the girl had protested.

" Oh, no ! I couldn't ! I've never done any modelling, and I'd be so scared in front of all those people that I'd be sure to do something stupid and clumsy. Please choose someone else."

Wisely, Mrs Stewart didn't press the point.

" But you will come to our first rehearsal tonight and fix our hair for us, won't you, Lucy ?"

" Oh, yes, you can rely on me for that," Lucy replied, with a confident smile. " I've got a book showing hair styles through the ages."

Anyone dropping in to Mrs Stewart's house that evening would have thought they'd stepped back about two hundred years in time. And the clothes were not all for the ladies, either !

" Now this costume was worn by a gentleman in the year 1790," Mrs Stewart was saying when Lucy arrived, " but Mrs Cunningham is going to wear it for us now. She's the right height and build, and when she's got the powdered wig on, even her husband won't recognise her !"

Amidst the laughter, Liz Cunningham, a tall, well-built girl, was dressed in tight, white trousers with white silk stockings and black shoes, a blue coat with long tails and a high, velvet collar. She sat down, rather gingerly, while Lucy tucked her hair underneath the white, curled wig so that none of it showed, and fastened the curls at the back with a broad, black velvet bow.

" Now, walk the length of the room," Mrs Stewart instructed. " Slowly, so that the audience can see how well the clothes have been preserved. Notice how the blue of the coat hasn't faded ? It fits very well, doesn't it ?"

When Mrs Cunningham had completed her slow promenade up the room and down again, Mrs Stewart spoke again.

" That was very good, Liz. Now, you're really one of a pair and you're supposed to be escorting a young lady to a ball, so will you please sit there until I find someone to wear the lady's dress. I was hoping Lucy . . . " She broke off suddenly. " Never mind, we'll dress some of the other ladies first. Here's a crinoline for a girl in Queen Victoria's reign."

So the evening continued, with dresses being tried on and hair styles arranged, amidst a buzz of excited comments.

" How did she eat anything when she wore this ?" came from some-one in a tightly-laced bodice.

" What a good thing this one didn't have to run for a bus ?" said another in a hooped skirt.

" Oh, Lucy ! My false curls are slipping," cried a lady from William IV's reign, in black taffeta and a dainty lace cap.

Lucy went about her work with quiet good humour until all the costumes, except one, were being worn.

" Now we've only the ball dress left," Mrs Stewart said at last. " I need someone small." She held up the delicate white muslin dress.

The dress was so simple, and yet so pretty, that Lucy forgot her shyness.

" I would like to try it on," she said, breathlessly.

Mrs Stewart turned to her with a smile.

" I'm so glad, dear," she said. " I've felt all along it's the one for you."

THE dress fitted Lucy perfectly. She had to arrange her own hair, but that wasn't difficult as it was already long and, parted in the centre, fell easily into two pairs of ringlets. Long white gloves, satin slippers and a tiny cap of white lace went with the outfit. But wasn't there something else needed to complete it ? Something to hold in her hand or suspend from her wrist ? Why, of course, a fan !

" I should have Miss Neilson's fan," Lucy exclaimed. " It would be just right, wouldn't it ?"

" It would !" Mrs Stewart agreed. " A young lady going to a ball in the eighteenth century would be sure to have her fan. Now, Lucy, I want you to imagine Mrs Cunningham is your partner. She's a handsome young man escorting you to your first ball. Think how you would feel as you take his arm."

Playing her part as well, Lucy's escort bowed to her with old world gallantry, while Lucy curtseyed unaware, as were all the others, that they were being observed from the doorway. Roy Stewart, thinking the rehearsal would be over, had come in just in time to see this little scene. He hesitated for only a moment then quickly and quietly went upstairs to his room.

But his dreams that night were strangely disturbed by a girl in a white dress and long, flaxen curls. A childhood sweetheart called Lucy, who had grown up into a lovely young woman. How could he have been so blind not to notice this before ! And how was he going to make amends for his behaviour at the sale in Miss Neilson's house ?

The Fashion Show, held at the Town Hall, was the highlight of Shopping Week. Mrs Stewart herself was to give the commentary, telling her audience something of the history and origin of each costume. Outside it was a dry, cold night, but inside the hall there was plenty of brightness, warmth and noisy chatter as people arrived early to get the best seats. There was much competition for the chairs immediately alongside the catwalk.

Behind the scenes, too, there was plenty of chatter as the amateur mannequins and the friends who'd come to help them to dress prepared for the evening. Lucy Boyd was much in demand with her hairdressing equipment, but fortunately her own dress was easy to slip on, unlike the crinolines and bustles of the Victorian era, so she was able to give plenty of attention to the other ladies. But where was Lucy's partner, Mrs Cunningham ?

Mrs Stewart, also, was wondering what had happened to Liz Cunningham as she went out into the frosty air to see if there was any sign of her car.

But it was Roy's car which stopped at the pavement edge and Roy himself who stepped out quickly and slammed the car door behind him.

"It's bad news, I'm afraid, Mother," he said. "Mrs Cunningham's just phoned. Liz has had a bad fall in the kitchen rushing to get ready to come here."

"Oh, dear, I am sorry," Mrs Stewart said. "Is she badly hurt? Is there anything we can do?"

Roy shook his head.

"I don't think it's anything serious, a black eye and some bruises but, of course, she can't be here tonight."

"Oh, well, we'll just have to change the programme a bit," Mrs Stewart said, with a resigned shrug. "Lucy will have to go on without a partner. What a pity! We all thought that little scene looked so natural, too. It would have stolen the show but never mind, it can't be helped."

She turned to go back into the hall, but Roy caught her arm.

"Mother! Could I take Liz's place?" he asked.

Mrs Stewart looked up at him in astonishment.

"You!" she exclaimed. "Well, why not? The costume was worn originally by a man about your age and size, wasn't it?"

Her eyes twinkled, and her face broke into a broad smile.

"Oh, Roy, it would be such fun! How sweet of you to suggest it. I won't say a word to anyone. I'll get the costume and you can change into it in the house. You'll be as quick as you can, won't you?"

IT was a happy, relaxed and smiling Mrs Stewart who addressed the audience that evening. That she loved her collection of historical costumes was soon apparent to everyone and her models, too, entered into the spirit of the evening as they stepped out confidently and promenaded slowly and gracefully to the end of the catwalk, curtseyed, turned and made their way back again to loud and appreciative applause.

When it was Lucy's turn, she stood for a moment in the centre of the stage while Mrs Stewart introduced her and described her dress. Miss Neilson's fan hung on her white-gloved wrist as she stepped off the stage and on to the catwalk.

"And so we watch Miss Lucinda Mary going to her first ball. Notice the simple lines of her dress and notice, too, the fan of Japanese silk, hand-painted, on sticks of ivory. No lady would think of going to a ball in those days without her fan!"

Lucy opened the fan and fluttered it expertly. She didn't feel shy, awkward or clumsy. In fact, she didn't feel like herself at all! In some strange way she felt as though she really had stepped back into the eighteenth century and taken on the personality of the girl who'd originally used the fan.

She remembered Mrs Stewart's instructions to turn at the end of the catwalk and face the audience on her left, then turn again and face those on her right. And then she was to look straight ahead to her partner who would be coming to meet her.

While she made her curtseys, Lucy could hear Mrs Stewart introducing her partner and describing his dress. So Liz Cunningham hadn't been too late, after all, was her relieved thought.

But when she looked up it wasn't Liz's face she saw, but the strong, lean features of a man she knew well. And he wasn't wearing the white, curled wig. His own dark hair met the high, velvet collar of the blue, cutaway coat. His eyes, as they met Lucy's, were tender and smiling.

" Roy !" Lucy's lips mouthed the word as, with fan fluttering, she sank into the required curtsey.

R OY STEWART bowed, courteous and correct. Then, with arms outstretched, he bent over Lucy and drew her to her feet. Drawing her small, gloved hand through his arm, he escorted her back to the stage.

Having reached the safety of the stage, she tried to draw away but Roy kept her close beside him while they acknowledged the enthusiastic clapping of the audience.

Bending down, he whispered to her.

" Lucy ! Once upon a time, when they were very young, two people loved each other. But they grew up, and drew apart.

" Then one evening something like magic happened. They stepped back in time and found each other again."

He paused, lifted her chin, and looked into her face.

" Is that true, Lucy ?" he asked, anxiously. " We have found each other again, haven't we ?"

With a flick of her wrist, Miss Lucinda Mary Boyd opened her fan and held it in front of her face. Then, lowering it a little, she looked at her suitor over the top of it with eyes warm and inviting which told him all he wanted to know.

Winter is past, soon life will begin anew.

by
ELSIE
DUNCAN

No Eagles for Us

DONALD MORRISON was writing a letter in his cottage above
the shore when a shaft from the setting sun sparkled on Alison
Ross's bicycle on the low shore road and he looked up.

Donald put down his pen and glanced quickly up at the ancient wall
clock, ticking slowly in the silence. From the window he had a clear
view of the harbour of land-locked Altnacreag, and his own boat, the
Moira, her half-deck piled high with lobster creels.

Beyond the harbour the sheltering narrows widened towards the
open sea, where black-fanged skerries, gold-capped in the lowering sun,
broke the ever-restless surface near to where three small isles wore the
golden halos of a September evening.

For all that he knew those skerries in times when their ragged teeth sent the sea driving in white spindrift, Donald looked at them now with softening eyes. He recalled evenings such as this when he had gone there with his father, taking a book along with him for the long run out and back again. His father had thoroughly approved of the book part of it, for if a boy was to pass the entrance examinations to university with a veterinary course in view, then he must take every chance for study.

As things were to turn out, Donald had never taken those exams. He hadn't yet completed his final year in Campbeltown Grammar School when his father had died suddenly. Donald had come home then, and had never gone back. His mother, who had been an invalid before the loss of her husband, had lived to see her son known as the most skilled lobster fisher on all the coast, and had died proud of his achievements.

A LISON dismounted and laid her cycle against the wooden fence where one of Donald's three cows scratched itself thoughtfully. With a friendly pat for the cow, she walked towards the gate, the movement of her head catching the low sunlight and striking flecks of gold from the dark cloud of hair that clustered above the creamy white of her neck.

From the window Donald tried, as lately he had tried over and over again, to believe that this demure assistant mistress in the village school could really have grown out of the thin-legged, ten-year-old Alison Ross whom he had allowed to help him dig for bait in the ebb— only because he couldn't get rid of her.

Not that he'd tried all that hard, Donald now admitted to himself. It was fine having someone who didn't mind carrying the bucket, and fine, too, having someone to listen while you talked of all the wonderful things you planned to do in the future. Not that you could be certain Alison believed such things would come about ; like him being decorated by the King for curing his favourite horse of a bad cough. What you could be sure of was that she would be there to listen.

The gate clicked, and Donald pushed back his mop of sun-bleached hair from above his eyes as he opened the door.

A brown calf standing outside kicked up its heels and bounded off in the direction of the stackyard.

" Best calves I've had in years," Donald commented, watching it go. " You're early, Alison, not that it matters. Maybe all the better. The last of the sun will still be on the reef, if we leave now."

Alison shook her dark hair so that gold lights danced in it again.

" Donald, I can't go out tonight. That's what I came down to tell you. You see, Mrs Christie only got Ian's letter today, and that was before she hurt her foot."

" Wait a minute !" Donald held up a hand. " What about Ian's letter, and who's hurt their foot?"

" Mrs Christie," Alison said slowly. " And in the letter it said that Ian is coming home this week."

Slowly Donald eased himself down on to a big flat stone that his grandmother had once used for her wash-tub, noting absently that the westering sun warmed it pleasantly.

" You may think me a bit slow on the uptake, Alison," he said, " but I'm afraid I just don't get the connection."

Alison smiled and hoisted herself on an empty bee-skep, tucking her knees beneath her kilted old cycling skirt.

" It's simple, Donald," she explained patiently. " Ian's landing at Prestwick on Thursday. All the way home from New York, for the first time in four years. Mrs Christie got his letter only this forenoon, just an hour before she slipped on the step-ladder and hurt her foot."

" I'm sorry about that," Donald said. " Only, I still don't see . . ."

" Where I come in?" Alison interrupted. " No, you wouldn't, of course. Who do you suppose is going to hang fresh curtains and patch up bits of faded wallpaper, and just polish up a little? Mrs Christie didn't like asking me, and, of course, I've only the evenings."

" Evenings?" Donald sounded incredulous. " More than one evening, then?"

Alison pursed her full lips.

" Men !" she muttered. " Can't you get it into your head that this is Ian's first visit home for four years ? And that his mother wants things just a bit special? After all, how many Altnacreag boys have got on as well as Ian?"

SINCE this wasn't a question that needed an answer, Alison didn't notice the sharp look Donald shot in her direction as he slid from the big, warm stone.

" Oh, well," he said. " Don't let me stop you. Anyway, I've my calves to see to before I go out. That's what I was going to do, to give you time to get down to the harbour."

Alison, too, slipped down from her perch, smoothing her faded skirt.

" Donald," she said softly, " I'm sorry this had to happen. I was looking forward all day to going out to the skerries with you, and on such an evening. Perhaps we can arrange another time?"

Donald laughed shortly.

" ' Times man may set,' " he quoted, " ' but tides are for the Lord.' You'll mind how old Mr Dunn hammered that into our heads at the Sunday school? I never could make head nor tail, at the time, what he meant by it !"

Alison smiled, relieved within herself that he seemed to understand how things had happened.

" And you weren't the most backward in the class," she reminded him.

" No," he agreed. " I wasn't, now I come to think of it."

Alison walked slowly towards the gate, taking a long time to secure the simple latch, as if half-hoping he might call out to her not to go. But when she lifted her eyes he just waved a careless hand, half-turning to go towards the stackyard.

She picked up her cycle quickly, lifted herself to the saddle, and, without a backward glance, pedalled swiftly off along the shore road.

No Eagles For Us

Donald Morrison didn't take more than the one step in the direction of the stackyard where his calves played in the last of the sun. Instead, he stood where he was, turning to watch Alison out of sight, deep thought in his eyes. When at last she turned the slight bend where the road inclined steeply upward to the main village, his shoulders lifted and fell again in a sigh expressive of those thoughts, before he turned on his heel to walk slowly back into the house.

On the low desk in the gable window lay the letter he had almost finished writing, when that shaft of sunlight had touched bright steel and slanted to his eyes.

He picked up the sheet and read it through. It wanted little now beyond his name at the end. Donald's unseeing hand reached to where he knew his pen lay in the same moment as, out beyond the sleeping skerries, his eye caught the low, red, deepening of the cloak of gold cast by the setting sun over the low hills of the dreaming isles.

Slowly, deliberately, he folded the letter in two, then tore it across, once and once again, carrying the strips to the smouldering embers of the kitchen fire. Then, whistling a jaunty air, he gathered the calves' pails from beneath the scullery shelf.

ALISON didn't look back or slow down till she knew for sure she was round the bend and out of sight of Donald's cottage.

It was only three hours since she had heard that Ian Christie was coming home, and she wondered now if she had been able to hide from Donald the excitement the news had set up within her heart.

From the age of four, when a road accident had deprived her of her father, there had been only two men in the life of Alison Ross. True, neither of those men had been older than six years old at the time, yet Alison still recalled her determination to cling to one or the other of them in turn.

She had played nurse in their doctor games, and often enough had acted in the more practical way of applying cold handkerchiefs to bleeding noses when the boys, as frequently happened, came to blows.

It had never occurred to Alison in those far-off days that there might ever be another kind of life for the three of them. When the two boys had finally deserted the village for the Grammar School she had been, as her mother had told her since, like a little ghost wandering alone. And when they came home on occasional week-ends, something had been lost that was never to be found again.

Vaguely, Alison knew that a gulf had opened between her and the two boys; a gulf that widened with the months and years, till, in her twelfth year, her mother had sent her off to school in Inverness.

At holiday times she saw her old companions again, but the old, easy relationship with them was over for ever. Anyway, Alison usually had a classmate home at the holidays, and the boys had their own pursuits, which, at that particular age, were for men only.

By the time Alison went to university in Glasgow, Ian Christie had already been in the city for two years, working hard with the big firm of exporters he had joined. Possibly on his mother's written suggestion,

45

he had called at the house where Alison lodged with two other girl students.

To her delight, and to the jealousy of her room-mates, he hadn't called just once as a duty, but had come at regular intervals to take her out to pictures, skating or dancing.

HERE began a completely new stage in the long relationship between Alison and the two boys. One of the boys, at any rate, for when she asked about Donald, Ian said he never heard of him nowadays and that, so far as he knew, Donald had failed to make the university entrance standard and had just stayed on in the croft.

Alison had been surprised. " Well, if a man has no ambition to get anywhere, I'm the last to blame him," Ian had said.

That he himself clearly intended to get somewhere was plain, even then, and Alison had listened eagerly as he told her of his plans for the future. They were not, she recalled, as wonderful as the great plans once outlined by Donald on the cold days on the muddy ebb.

And she was happy for Ian, as his plans took concrete form with dazzling speed ; yet a little unhappy on the day he told her of his promotion to the firm's New York branch. For by now Ian wasn't one of two boys but a man, handsome, assured and confident.

The evening before Ian went to the airport to catch his flight they had sat together in the small café where they had gone on the first evening he had taken her out. Alison had found herself wrapped in the strange, desolate mood which had overtaken her long ago when the boys had first left Altnacreag for the Grammar School.

" This is the second time I've lost you, Ian," she had remarked after a long silence.

" And the first time I've really found you, Alison," he had answered. " Don't forget, those Atlantic planes fly both ways, you know !"

And with that Alison had to be content. For a time they wrote, but, as the years passed and both were busy, the letters slowed, then ceased altogether.

Six months ago Alison had, to her delight, been appointed to the school at Altnacreag. It was wonderful living in the schoolhouse that had once seemed so huge, and recognising children as the sons and daughters of boys and girls from her own school days here. And it was good to meet again with folk she had known so well.

Among the last of old friends with whom she renewed aquaintance was Donald Morrison. He hadn't called at the schoolhouse as others had, and Alison guessed he was busy with lambs at the time, alone on his croft.

Inverness, now generally known as the capital of the Highlands, makes an ideal centre for touring the beautiful surrounding countryside. A short drive takes you to Loch Ness, home of the legendary monster. But in spite of its long history, the town has a bright future, especially in the growing industry of tourism. Recreations of mountain, valley and seaside are all near at hand.

Inverness   J. Campbell Kerr

Then one evening on a quiet walk by the harbour, a big man in a blue jersey had scrambled from a boat up over the wall of the break-water and straightened his long bulk in front of where she stood.

" Donald !" Alison had almost screamed.

" Alison !" His eyes had lit in surprise as he looked at her, and she had a delightful feeling that he liked what he saw.

Companionably at ease, they walked together to where their ways parted.

" Funny what time does," Alison had remarked inconsequently. " Remember how I was going to be a nurse and you a vet? We both changed our minds."

Donald had nodded. " You haven't changed much otherwise," he added after a moment.

" Neither have you," Alison said.

Yet, after they had gone on their own ways in the softly-gathering twilight, she had turned her head to look at him striding along the shore road, a heavy net across one broad shoulder. She wasn't so sure then if what she had said was true. Oddly, Ian's words of four years ago had come back to her :

" If a man has no ambition to get anywhere . . ."

IN the months that followed, Alison saw Donald often. After church on Sundays they fell into the way of walking home together, and Donald was ready enough, on her mother's insistence, to take a cup of tea at the schoolhouse before going home to see to his ever-waiting animals.

Often, too, on a fine Saturday while he repaired his lobster creels by the breakwater he would look up to find her impish face framed in its soft, dark cloud, looking down at him. Usually she would have a basket loaded with buttered scones, slices of her mother's home-made cake, and a flask of tea.

Once she hadn't taken the flask. Instead, they had gone along the shore to a sheltered, well-remembered cove not far from the ebb where once they had gathered bait for the hand lines, and there they had lit a fire of scented driftwood, boiling the tea in a pan. Alison had got smoke in her hair and smudges on her face, and though she didn't try to analyse her thoughts, knew that never since the days when the boys had allowed her to help build the fire had she been so happy.

It was the following Sunday, on their leisurely way from church, that Donald had wondered if Alison would like to come out with him the next evening while he lifted and laid his creels by the distant skerries where, even in fine weather, the lazy waves gathered for the long roll to the coast.

Alison had looked forward to this outing with almost a child's excitement. She had only once been out in the *Moira*, when Donald's father had allowed her to come for a short run and the two boys had made their displeasure at her intrusion very clear indeed.

And now, that afternoon, Mrs Christie's note appealing for help had been handed in at the schoolhouse.

On the Thursday the telephone in the schoolhouse rang. Since it was nearly time for Alison to go back to her afternoon classes her mother picked up the receiver, but almost at once handed it to Alison.

" Alison?" Donald's voice reached her before the instrument touched her hair. " I know you must be almost due back in school, but that Mrs MacGilp was in this kiosk and I thought she was going to talk for ever !"

" I'm surprised you ever got in at all !" She glanced up at the clock. " I've got a full five minutes."

" Good." Donald sounded relieved. " It'll not take that time. The tide's exactly right for the skerries tonight, better than Monday really. Would you like to come out this evening, a bit after six?"

" Listen, Donald. I can't come out, not tonight. I promised to go to Tarbert to meet Ian off the Glasgow bus. Can't we fix another evening to go out in the *Moira*? "

" No, we can't, Alison. That's just a part of what I wanted to talk to you about. Only it doesn't matter now. Maybe it never did matter at all."

" Donald—wait !" She could sense his receiver dropping towards its rest. " Don't go ! There's a party tomorrow night. Mrs Christie's giving a sort of welcome home for Ian—and I know you're to be invited. Can we talk then? We could walk up together about seven."

This time his short laugh came clearly over the wire.

" Funny," he began reminiscently, " funny how I never used to know what old Mr Dunn was getting at. You remember. ' Times man may set.' "

The burr of the dialling tone told her he had replaced his receiver on the last word. Alison crossed the sunlit road to the school, her soft eyes deeply troubled.

The afternoon flew quickly, however, and with school over there was little time for any thought other than to get ready quickly for the run to Tarbert.

The moment Ian stepped off the bus in Tarbert the whole character of the village seemed to undergo a change. From being sleepy and colourless, as Alison's still troubled mind made it seem, it assumed the bright, brisk outlook Ian's vital, energetic presence had always given to his surroundings.

NEXT evening Alison didn't wait for Donald to walk up with her to the Christies' house. From the crossroads below the school, one glance at the harbour showed her the *Moira*'s mooring buoy deserted and swinging tuggingly in the short, cold-edged gusts that a sudden change in the fine weather had brought.

The party was a success. Ian was the perfect host, polished, poised, confident and handsome, too, so that the oldest lady there, who was seventy-four, fell in love with him straight away.

As for Alison, the magnetism that in her college days, had drawn her into a new relationship with the boy she had known, returned easily.

D

Perhaps more strongly, for here was the finished man, yet still filled with a boy's enthusiasm.

By midnight, when Alison suddenly realised the time and Ian got briskly to his feet to walk home with her, the door was almost snatched from his hand by a shrieking blast from the west.

" It's a wild night, Alison," he remarked. " I can't imagine why you didn't think to take your car up."

" I like it this way !" Alison declared, tossing her dark locks loose to the wind. " Look, you don't have to come out. There's a full moon and I'll run all the way !"

" You'd get blown over the harbour wall !"

L EANING into the screaming night, Alison and Ian fought their way down toward the crossroads overlooking the harbour.

" I ought to have known !" Ian shouted into her ear. " I should never have come over at this time of year. Look, Alison, don't you get sick of this place at times? You'd do all right in New York, let me tell you. You've got looks, for a start."

Alison stood stock still, pointing a cold, dripping hand, every thought but one driven from her mind by what she saw.

" The *Moira* !" she screamed against the gale. " She was out and she's not back, the mooring's empty. Donald must be caught out in this somewhere !"

" Oh, he'll be all right," he spoke confidently as always. " He knows the coast well. He'll be in shelter long ago !"

" How can you know that?" Alison's voice was so sharply-edged that the man beside her started in surprise. She herself was mildly astonished. It was as if the flooding moonlight had sent a greater light into her heart so that, even through the driving storm, she saw Donald's face as clearly as if he had been standing there beside her.

" I'm going over to the coastguard's house," Alison announced with determination. " He'll know whether to call out the lifeboat."

The coastguard's house stood on the promontory to the south of the village beyond the ebb. To reach it Alison had first to turn into the narrow lane of store sheds above the harbour wall. Here it was easier to run, and she did so, her breath returning as she gathered speed. Then she almost ran full tilt into the protectively outspread arms of a tall, gleaming oilskin-coated figure walking along the lane from the opposite end.

" Alison ! What in all the world are you doing here?"

" Donald ! Oh, you're safe ! I was so frightened."

For a time Alison could only sob, gaspingly, with relief. Then she told him ; the party, the storm, the moonlight and the missing boat.

" I sold her, Alison," Donald said gently. " It was too tangled a story to tell you on the phone that day. I sold her to a man in Campbeltown, and took her down there late this afternoon.

" Donald, you sold your boat ! But you're not giving up the fishing? You can't do that !"

" The thing is, Alison, I've been offered a job on a big nature conservancy.

" Oh, but that means going away, Donald !" Alison's disappointment was clear in the wet half-light of the once again hidden moon.

" I tore the letter up, Alison," he said in a flat tone. " I had already agreed on a price for my boat so I couldn't go back on that, even if I wanted. But, as it happens, I've been looking for a newer boat for a long time and I saw the very one today."

" Donald, when you tore up the letter. Was it anything to do with me?"

" In a way," he said thoughtfully. " The queer thing is, that applying for the post to begin with was very much because of you, Alison. It was the kind of post," he smiled wryly again, " for a man who means to get somewhere.

" Then you came down that evening and perched yourself on the empty bee skep. If I took the post I was never going to see you sitting there again.

" Do you recall once, Alison, long, long ago, that I told you I had an eagle's nest up on that crag and I would take you up to see it?"

" Well," Donald went on, " it wasn't really an eagle. Just a kestrel hawk. I've wondered sometimes if you knew?"

" Yes, Donald, I think I guessed at the time. But, you must see, I was never the one to want eagles. Eagles are what Ian calls ' doing things big.' Kestrel hawks, well, you just take me to see your kestrels any day you like, Donald. I'm waiting."

She spoke softly, watching his eyes widen in something between disbelief and understanding.

" That day on the phone I nearly told you," he began, and stopped again as the moon flooded the narrow lane with its light.

" You could always try the phone box again," Alison said with a mischievous light in her brown eyes.

Donald laughed aloud, looking upward at the clearing sky.

" Mrs MacGilp might be there !" he declared. " It's late, Alison, but I'm not taking a chance like that, ever again !"

The promise of spring is here with the lambs.

DOREEN WATTS made her way through the new bus station at Anderston towards the bus that would take her to her brother's filling station near Windyridge.

Though normally sociable, Doreen was glad she knew no one on the bus as the short run beyond the city boundary was just what she needed to think carefully about the delicate task suddenly thrust upon her.

A letter had arrived this morning from her cousin in Belgium. Vicky had a good job there, but in all other ways she was highly undependable.

When she left Windyridge, she had been engaged to one of the local farmers, Drew Pearson. Doreen had met him, as had all the Watts family, and the news of the engagement had been well received even though there was an age gap of seven years between Vicky and her fiancé.

" All the better to wed an older man," one of their grandmothers had pronounced, speaking out of her own experience. " And Vicky needs a steadying influence. She's far too flighty for her own good."

" Flighty ?" Doreen had returned lightly. " She has a far better job than mine. Vicky's got her head screwed on the right way."

Now, as the bus started off, she wondered if her loyalty had been misplaced.

Vicky's letter that morning had begun calmly enough.

So you're going to work for Edwin for a bit, to help straighten out his books. I wish you luck, for although I tried to unravel them in the summer, I got nowhere fast.

But I'm writing to you, Doreen, for another reason. The note enclosed is for Drew and the ring's inside as well. I've explained all about why I can't marry him, but I thought that it would be a good idea to ask you to take the letter to Drew. Perhaps you'll find a way of softening the blow. There isn't anyone else, but I've decided I'm just not cut out to be a farmer's wife, especially a farmer in Windyridge . . .

How considerate, had been Doreen's first wry thought. And how inconsiderate to saddle her with the responsibility of letting Drew down lightly. What on earth did Vicky suppose she was going to do ?

She was biting her lip in vexed exasperation when the bus stopped to pick up some more passengers. Most went inside, but one young man paused in the act of running upstairs and his dark eyes encountered Doreen's. Although she was certain they had never met, genuine recognition seemed to be in his face as he changed his mind about going aloft. Instead, he made his way down the swaying bus, smiling at her in friendly fashion.

" Doreen ? Doreen Watts ?"

" Yes, but I'm afraid . . ."

" You're right. We haven't met, but you're so like your brother, Edwin, that I felt pretty certain. Anyhow, he told me you might be travelling around this time." He sat down beside her. " I'm Jason Leslie. Now do you know who I am ?"

If A Letter

She was shaking her head when all at once she remembered her sister-in-law telling her that they had a new man in the garage, Jason Leslie. She had gathered that both Sal and Edwin were pleased at how well he was getting on.

" I see that the penny has dropped." He grinned, fishing in his coat pocket for the fare. " There ought to be a discount for those of us who

by
John
Cochrane

don't make you climb the stairs," he told the waiting conductor, who grinned as he punched a ticket and presented it to the younger man.

" What's yours, miss ?"

" Oh, allow me," Jason Leslie cut in, his face apologetic. " And forgive me for not checking you had a ticket. I assumed you'd got it earlier."

" I expect I ought to have had," she said placatingly to the conductor. " I'm sorry. I was probably daydreaming when you came round before."

A FTER he had stumped off, Doreen stole a look at the man beside her. He had a strong profile with direct dark eyes that held hers when he turned to ask how long she intended to stay in Windyridge.

" That all depends on my brother," she answered. Vicky hadn't been joking when she forecast that sorting out the garage books might be far from simple. Anyway, she was between jobs just now and she loved the little town with its friendly people.

" They told me you'd be in the office for a spell. Believe me, you'll make a difference."

" I mean to do my best."

He smiled reminiscently.

" It was a big help when your sister was through in the summer."

" My sister ?" Doreen was momentarily perplexed. " Oh, my cousin, you mean." She wondered if it had been Vicky he was expecting to see on this evening bus. Engaged or not, her cousin was an incorrigible flirt, and she would have made good use of her time when she and Jason were working together some months earlier.

Another possibility struck Doreen suddenly. Was it because of Jason that Vicky was now calling off her engagement ?

" You saw a lot of each other ?"

She wasn't quite sure why she put the question. Was it merely to make polite conversation on the shared journey, or was it pure curiosity about what lay behind Vicky's sudden change of heart ?

" Naturally." Jason peered through the window at the trees and fields rushing past, plainly seeking a landmark.

" Naturally ?" she queried, amused. " Didn't Drew mind ?"

" Drew Pearson ? Oh, I don't think he had a chance to. Your cousin Vicky has a mind of her own, and if she felt like accepting an invitation for an evening out, all the farmers in the country wouldn't have stopped her."

Doreen gave him a cool look.

" Most men refrain from asking an engaged girl out."

" Oh, dear. I seem to have blotted my copybook with you, and I've only known you for ten minutes !"

" Not at all," she returned stiffly. " What you do, Mr Leslie, is no concern of mine."

" And of even less interest," he finished ruefully.

Probably he would be delighted to hear of the broken engagement, but that was something she couldn't disclose before Drew knew about it.

While the man beside her kept up a stream of light chat about films and television programmes they had both seen, she thought of Drew Pearson with compassion.

Less and less she liked the idea of being the one to hand Vicky's letter to him. Worse than that, Vicky had added a sentence in her covering letter to make Doreen all the more uncomfortable.

It won't seem so cruel if you're there when he gets my letter, Doreen. Drew always liked you, and I know he admires you tremendously. He has every reason to do so. Ask him to think kindly of your cousin, Vicky.

"Next stop's ours," Jason said quietly, and with a start Doreen realised she must have been engrossed in her own thoughts for too long.

Though it was dusk, the country road was well lit by a bright, compact-looking garage and filling station. The moment the bus had appeared, a young woman ran from the bungalow nearby to welcome Doreen.

"Hello and welcome. You, too, Jason. Like to join us for supper?"

"I'd like that," he agreed readily, "but my landlady will have something ready for me. I'd better ask Edwin if he needs a hand before I leave."

He left them, and Sal guided her sister-in-law into the house.

"Come and tell me all your news."

"Everybody's fine back home. Mum and Dad send their love to you all. The children will be in bed by now, I suppose."

"Yes, thank goodness," their mother said fervently. "And believe me, it wasn't easy, especially when they knew you were coming. You're their favourite aunt."

"I'm their only aunt." Doreen laughed as she took off her coat and went over to warm her hands at the fire. "Anything I can do to help?"

"Not a thing. Once Edwin comes in, we can have our meal. What do you think of Jason?"

"I don't really know," Doreen protested, amused. "We've only just met. He seems all right. A bit on the talkative side, maybe."

Sal looked surprised.

"It must be you that brings out the chatty streak then. He's generally considered the strong, silent type around here."

"How did he strike Vicky?" Doreen inquired before she could think better of it.

Sal's voice took on the slightly defensive tone she used when speaking of someone she didn't completely approve of.

"Vicky? Oh, they got along fine, as far as I know." She looked speculatively at Doreen. "What's the news from abroad?"

FORTUNATELY her brother came in at that moment and Doreen was able to postpone a full answer.

"Hi, Edwin! Business good?"

"Business is splendid. The books are slightly askew."

"Chaotic would be a better word," his wife put in with a smile at Doreen. "You haven't come a minute too soon."

"Serves me right for working in a C.A.'s office." Doreen nodded.

"Come on, let's eat," her brother suggested. "I'll have to go back to the filling station and let Jason go home."

" So he did stay. I'll make up a tray for him and Doreen can take it over."

" Give her a chance," Edwin protested. " She's hardly in the door and you've got her working already. I'll take it over to him."

Doreen chuckled at her sister-in-law's thwarted look as he hurried off.

" That'll teach you to try your old matchmaking tricks," she teased fondly. " Anyway, you're wasting your time. He's not my type and I'm quite sure I'm not his."

When her brother returned he brought back an unexpected guest.

" This is a surprise," Sal welcomed him brightly. " Sit down and have something with us. No need to introduce you two, is there ?"

" None whatever." Doreen shook her head. " How are you, Drew?"

" Well, thanks. Good to see you back again, Doreen."

" Drew brought in one of the trucks," Edwin explained. " It's a small job that can be done in half an hour."

THE letter from Vicky was burning a hole in Doreen's handbag, but she shrank from giving it to him just then. Surely waiting till next day would do no harm.

Nevertheless, she knew if he asked how Vicky was she would have to hand over the letter. She wished with all her heart she wasn't involved in this tricky situation.

" Vicky seems to be enjoying life in Brussels," Drew remarked over the meal. " I had a letter last week. She seems to be having a wonderful time. Finished up in the usual way, wish you were here !"

" You'll just have to pack up and go over there for a holiday," Sal said warmly. " Anyway, you deserve a change, Drew."

" I might just do that." He nodded thoughtfully.

A phone call from the garage informed them the truck was repaired now and ready for removal.

" Now, this time you must pay us a visit at Honeywalk, Doreen," Drew insisted. " No excuses this time. How about coming over tomorrow for lunch ?"

Doreen knew the others were looking at her in surprise for being so slow to accept the warm invitation.

" Thanks, Drew. Maybe once I've got the books worked out."

" Oh, nonsense," her brother scoffed. " Another day isn't going to matter. You go over and see Mrs Pearson. She'll be delighted to have a chat with you."

" I'll come over in the runabout and pick you up, say about twelve," Drew offered.

Doreen could hardly sleep that night for thinking of the hurt she must inflict on Drew next day.

She awoke nervy and ill at ease and was soon aware that Sal was looking curiously at her.

" You're certainly needing this holiday, Doreen. You're as jumpy and nervous as a kitten."

" Sorry, Sal." Doreen smiled apologetically, having to shout above the clamour of the children. " I think I'll take these two down to the village this morning and give you some peace."

Five-year-old Sara danced with joy when she heard she was being taken to the village. Her brother, Tim, two years older, took his pleasures more seriously, but brightened when he learned there would be a visit to the sweet shop. He was even happier when he saw his hero in the courtyard of the filling station.

" Hi, Jason," Tim declared, man-to-man. " We've got to go to the village."

" Do you good having to walk for a change, young man."

" Aunt Doreen and Sara will have to walk as well."

" In that case, I'll consider giving you all a lift."

WITH the children securely locked in at the back, Jason looked at his passenger beside him.

" At a guess, I'd say you were a little less than pleased over the new arrangement."

" It isn't that at all. It's just that I have a bit of a problem on my mind."

" Anything I can help with ?"

" No one can help me. It's simply something unpleasant I have to do."

" Like tell Drew Pearson his girl isn't coming back ?"

" Would you mind explaining that extraordinary statement ?"

" A lucky guess. Drew's a stayer, but Vicky changes her mind with every wind that blows. I had the feeling she'd call the whole thing off one of these days, but at least I gave her credit for having courage enough to face the man when she did it."

The children had a marvellous time window-shopping. Then Jason took them into the sweet shop and, despite her protests, insisted on buying gifts for themselves and their mother.

Soon the children had been restored to their mother and, while Jason had a cup of coffee, Doreen got ready for her visit to the farm. Drew's mother was an old friend and she was looking forward to having a chat with her about days gone by.

" Well, all set ?" Jason asked, getting to his feet when she returned to the sitting-room.

" About as set as a jelly with too much water in it."

" When in doubt, bide a wee," he reminded her.

" What would you do, in my place ?" Doreen asked quietly.

" Knowing Vicky and the way she can change like a chameleon, I'd be inclined to get in touch with her and ask if she really wants that letter to be given to Drew."

" What a good idea, if I had a plane to nip over to Brussels."

" There's an old-fashioned thing called the telephone."

At ten minutes to twelve Doreen heard Vicky's voice.

" Doreen, you marvellous girl ! Did you get my cable then ?"

" No, I didn't. What did it say ?"

" To hold everything. The minute the letter was in the post I had doubts about what I'd done, and then it dawned on me what an idiot I was being . . ."

" You can say that again !"

" What's that ? Can't you hear me ?"

" I said," Doreen spoke the words very slowly, " you're a prize idiot, Vicky Watts, and you don't deserve anyone as nice as Drew Pearson. If I had any sense I'd give him your silly letter regardless."

" You wouldn't, would you ?"

" Let's say I will if you ever do anything so silly again. Now, what do you want me to do about that enclosure ? Keep it for you or return it ?"

" I'm due some leave soon." Vicky sounded chastened. " Be a dear and keep the ring safe for me, and Doreen . . ."

" Yes ?"

" This'll be our secret, just between us. All right ?"

" I'm not likely to spread it around."

JASON was outside in the hall when Doreen hung up. When their eyes met, she nodded relievedly.

" It's all right. Thanks for that brainwave about phoning her, Jason. I'll never be able to thank you."

" Oh, I don't know," he said thoughtfully. " I'll think of something, like asking you out to a theatre in town some evening."

" I'll be looking forward to it. Goodness, look at the time. I mustn't be late for the farm lunch. Mrs Pearson likes people to be there on time."

" You'll be there all right," he assured her, taking her arm.

" I'd better tell Sal," she began.

" I've seen to that as well. Anyway, she's busy feeding her family."

" You're incredible, Jason. Really incredible."

" I was hoping you'd discover it soon," he returned modestly, but grinning so broadly she simply had to burst out laughing.

" Come on," Jason encouraged her, as the engine revved. " Time and the Pearsons wait for no man or woman. Hop in."

Flowers bloom and birds sing in my garden.

CHRISTMAS was upon them, but Trudy Mair was no wiser as to who had sent the anonymous gift.

It had arrived beautifully parcelled in festive paper, tied with professional-looking bows. Inside was the handbag of soft brown leather, with the donor's lucky penny tucked within, but no card.

Someone somewhere would be expecting a note of thanks, or at the very least a phone call of appreciation for such a splendid present. As the days passed, Trudy began to feel more and more anxious, particularly when other things kept arriving from people she had earmarked in her mind as possible senders of the puzzle gift.

Phil Campbell, for instance. They had been going out for some months now and, before Christmas, he had kept asking her what she would like as a gift.

In the end, she told him about a new book to be published in mid-December by one of her favourite writers.

The Mystery Gift

BY
RUTH
SINCLAIR

" Good." He nodded approvingly. " Then that's what I'll get you."

" Another one off the list," she teased.

Phil had reacted strongly to the handbag's arrival, his dark eyes unusually keen and probing.

Each time they met, he would ask if she had tracked down the sender, until it began to get on her nerves.

" Oh, give over, do. I wish I hadn't mentioned it to you."

" Sorry. Am I becoming a bore ?"

Waiting in the ticket queue for the film they had chosen to see in Christmas week, she squeezed his arm lightly.

" Don't be huffy, Phil. Let's forget about the mystery. I'm getting tired of it."

But was that quite true, she wondered, as they found their way to the seats in the circle. There was a little, tremulous feeling of excitement when she pondered on the identity of the unknown admirer, as Phil termed him.

Nevertheless, it was fun to speculate about who could have sent it. There was Lloyd Grainge who had recently moved to the district and had appeared in the Youth Club a couple of times, causing much heart flutterings amongst the unattached members and even some that were going steady or engaged.

Ray Christie was another and much more likely possibility, for in days gone by they had been out together, though it had turned out to be one of these romances that somehow never quite got off the ground.

The men in the office were married or engaged, and had trouble enough coping with the buying of gifts for their own womenfolk without bothering to send a handbag to one of the typing pool.

MISS MAIR."
With a start, Trudy realised she had been daydreaming again, and this time in the middle of dictation from one of the firm's partners.

" I'm so sorry, Mr Casey. I'm afraid I just . . ."

" Was thinking of something else, obviously." With a twinkle, he went on, " Or somebody else is more likely. Well, it's Christmas week, after all, one can't expect the same concentration."

Patiently, he repeated the special instructions concerning a letter he wanted sent by recorded delivery.

He had specially requested the supervisor to send Trudy Mair as her work had been so neat and accurate previously. Apart from that spell of absentmindedness, she proved herself to be equally dependable this afternoon, though his eagle eye spotted one small typing mistake when she brought in the finished letter for signature.

" I'm sure you'll manage to change it neatly, my dear. Oh, by the way." He reached into a drawer of his desk and produced a large box of chocolates. " A very happy Christmas, Miss Mair, and thank you for all your good work since you came."

" Thank you. Thank you very much, Mr Casey. I hope you have a happy Christmas, too."

While Trudy was making the change in the typing, the phone rang. It was Phil to remind her about their evening date.

"I haven't forgotten," she assured him, "but I can't stop to chat right now. Mr Casey's waiting for this particular letter. It's pretty important."

"He ought to have dictated it earlier, then," Phil grumbled lightly.

"He did, but things have been a bit hectic in the office today."

That was putting it mildly, considering the entire staff had more or less downed tools after the mid-afternoon tea break which somehow had extended itself into a gay, informal party.

"No gatecrashers allowed, I suppose?"

"You suppose right. No, Phil, it's for staff only, but I'll see you this evening. 'Bye for now."

NEVERTHELESS, Phil was waiting for her outside the office and as usual, Trudy's heart lifted at the sight of him, standing there with his coat collar turned up against the frost.

"Hi!" He greeted her with a grin. "Enjoy the party?"

"It was all right. I feel bad about you standing out here in the cold, though."

"That's why I didn't tell you I'd be picking you up when I rang." He tucked her arm into his and nodded at the envelope she was carrying. "Is that for the mail? It won't arrive in time for Christmas now, I'm afraid."

"It's Mr Casey's important letter. I offered to hand it in to his client."

"Good for you." He relieved her of the shopper in which was stowed the box of chocolates and the office gift drawn from the barrel. It was a handy clothes brush which no doubt would prove useful in the future. "Where to, then?"

"The usual bus, Phil. The letter's for someone in the next street to where I stay, so it won't take us far out of our way."

As they stood waiting for the bus, she asked what sort of day he'd had.

"So so. Like most places, I suppose, there was precious little work done in the afternoon."

"Betty and May probably got showered with gifts."

They were the only girls in a section filled with draughtsmen and tracers, and she could imagine them both struggling homewards burdened down with office presents.

Phil grinned reminiscently.

"May got a smashing handbag this Christmas, but she knows who it's from, her boy friend."

"I thought you'd never ask if I'd found out about mine," she teased, dimpling at his next question.

"And have you?"

"No."

To change the subject she told him about the silly error she had made in her typing that afternoon.

"One letter in a word can make a big difference," he agreed, helping her alight at the stop nearest to the address on the envelope. Suddenly he snapped his fingers.

" That's it, Trudy. That could be exactly it."

" What are you talking about ?"

" Suppose that package was meant for someone with a name the same as yours, or even slightly different ?"

" Living at my address ?" she asked sceptically. " That's hardly likely, or if it was, I'd know about it surely."

She felt a little resentful about losing that tremulous feeling. The handbag was a handsome one, but she would have handed it over without a qualm if she knew for certain it wasn't for her, but she'd be disappointed to give up the mystery and the thrill of tantalising herself by wondering just who could have sent it.

" Don't look at me like that." He smiled at her. " It's as though I'd taken chocolate from a baby."

" So I'm a baby now. Thanks a lot."

HUFFILY Trudy turned into the close indicated on the envelope, peering at the name on each door.

" You're sweet," he whispered, pulling her close. " Have I told you lately that I love you ?"

" Cue for a song, by the sound of it." She giggled.

" Aren't you ever serious ?"

" Oh, yes, when it's something important."

She regretted that when his arms dropped away from her.

" I didn't mean to be hurtful, Phil. I was just saying the first wisecrack that came into my head. I realise now how silly it was, how unfair."

They kissed on the landing, a lingering, tender kiss that seemed all the sweeter because from someone's radio they could hear a crooner singing, *I'm Dreaming of a White Christmas.*

Pulling apart reluctantly, they went on with the search, finally discovering the correct name two stairs farther up.

There was no one at home and, after a second's indecision, Trudy dropped the letter through the brass box.

" That's that then. Do you think it might be worth while looking around for someone with a name like mine, as you suggested, Phil ?"

" You might need a fine toothcomb," he teased her, squeezing her waist before they emerged to a frost sparkling night. " Well, it's a pastime we can keep in mind whenever we've a few hours to spare. Meantime, let's get you home. You must be starving."

" How about you ? Like to come in and have tea with us ?"

" Your mum won't mind ?"

" You know she won't. You're her blue-eyed boy, aren't you ?"

" I just want to be yours."

The local shops were open late for Christmas shopping, and everywhere was thronged with last-minute buyers.

Suddenly Trudy stopped in her tracks.

" What's wrong ?" Phil inquired.

" You see that lady over there, the one outside the fruiterers ?"

" Yes. What about her."

He looked across at a woman in her sixties who was studying the boxed tangerines while she made up her mind whether or not to buy them.

" That," Trudy told him, " happens to be someone called Moir. Miss Emily Moir, and I've just remembered she stays in the same number of street as I do, but at a different address."

" Moir . . . Mair." Phil looked at her keenly. " Think there's a chance of a mix-up having been made ? Well, why not ask her ?"

TRUDY knew the older woman very slightly, having once handed in a bunch of flowers from the church when Miss Moir was recovering from a stay in hospital, but she turned at once with a pleased smile.

" Hello, my dear. A Merry Christmas to you, too, when it comes. I was just wondering if I should have a box of these, in case my nephew comes over with his family next week."

" I haven't seen you travelling into town for a bit," Trudy remarked, aware that Phil had been left shivering outside a toyshop, and anxious not to keep him too long.

" Well, that's because I'm retired now, a lady of leisure," Miss Moir chuckled appreciatively. " And very thankful I am, too, not to have to roll out of bed early these cold mornings. Takes a bit of getting used to, though — retirement, I mean."

" I hope you got something very special at the presentation," Trudy said softly, knowing the older woman had spent almost all her working life with the same firm. Was it at all possible, she was wondering, that Phil was right about the handbag having been sent to the wrong address?

" By any chance were you expecting to receive a handbag this week ? " Trudy asked, feeling a little foolish. " I know it's maybe a silly question, but . . ."

" It's anything but silly," Miss Moir said swiftly. " I can't imagine how you know, my dear, but some of the agents in the office sent me a beautiful bag as a farewell

A WORD FOR LIVING

HIS wife couldn't believe it!

Her husband in the attic, reading the Bible!

" It's my mother's Bible." He spoke quietly. He had found it in an old trunk, wrapped in her lace shawl.

On the fly-leaf: " Margaret Wyllie." Two words unlocked for him the Book he had once dismissed as dead men's tales, and refused to believe otherwise.

Strangely compelled, he was reading, as often after his father's death, he remembered her doing. Finding courage to fend for the family. How worn the pages were!

Not " dead men's tales " for her, but a word for living.

Where others failed, a beloved hand had reached from the past to open for him the living Word of God!

Rev. T. R. S. Campbell

gift. Their card arrived but unfortunately the bag didn't, unless it's been delayed with the Christmas mail. I haven't given up hope that it may still reach me."

" It'll reach you this very evening," Trudy laughed, going on to explain matters. Any regret she might have felt at parting with the pleasant mystery was more than made up for by the delighted look on the other's face.

" You've really made my Christmas, Trudy. However can I thank you ?"

" You've taken a load off my mind, and Phil's. That's my boy friend waiting for me over there. I'd better say cheerio for now."

" He looks very nice."

" He is very nice."

SPEEDING across to him she sang out :
    " Your hunch was right, Phil. The bag does belong to Miss Moir. You must have second sight, or something."

" I don't know about second sight but frostbite, oh, yes. I thought you were never going to stop gabbing, you and your friend."

" I said we'd bring the present round this evening, Phil. Was that all right ?"

He grinned down at her.

" Anything you say is all right with me, Trudy, as if you didn't know."

" She said we'd really made her Christmas. It was a bit touching, I thought."

" I can tell you it's made mine. Now I don't have to worry my head over that unknown admirer, or have I ? Maybe this whole business of Miss Moir is simply a gigantic cover-up. My guess is you only went over to wish her a happy Christmas."

" How did you guess ?" she teased back, slipping her hand through his arm.

Here is peace, on the hill beside the loch.

It's An Ill Wind

BY KATHLEEN KINMOND

ISLA LIVINGSTONE was scarcely inside the house when Mrs Smith started telling her about the reunion.

Isla was fond of the little widow with whom she'd been staying for over a year. Mrs Smith's husband had once been manager of the bank where Isla worked, and they had taken to each other from the first.

The older woman loved hearing about Isla's various boy friends for, with her shining hair, tawny eyes and slim figure, the girl had plenty to pick and choose from.

All the same, Mrs Smith wasn't terribly keen on her latest admirer, Norman Bennett, who worked in the same bank as Isla. He'd started

as a boy with her husband and she'd asked Ted Simpson one evening how he was getting on.

"He's a clever youngster," Ted had said, "and one who should go far. But he won't mind whose toes he stands on on the way up."

Now, as the two women settled down for their evening meal, Isla asked for more details about the reunion.

"It's the Girl Guides in Lochside, the little town where I was born and brought up," Mrs Smith explained. "I was a Guide there, and a Brownie officer for eleven years!

"I became an officer as a teenager, and then carried on after I was married, and even for a few years after Roberta was born. Now I see from a paper cutting someone sent me, they are having a reunion dinner for their golden anniversary next month, and I'd just love to go."

"Why not? How far away is Lochside?"

"About two and a half hours' driving. There's only one thing, though. I'd rather stay for the night than return in the dark, and it would mean leaving you overnight."

"Don't let that worry you." The young girl laughed. "Lassie and I will be all right here together."

She patted the sleek head of the collie lying on the floor.

"Well, it's on a Friday evening, so you could have a long lie next morning."

"A Friday evening? Why not stay for the weekend if you want to?"

THERE was another reason why Connie Smith wanted to go home to the reunion, and that was to see Myrtle Munro. They'd been Guides together and then worked in the Brownies. Myrtle had been Brown Owl first, then when she'd married Willie Sutherland, Connie had taken over.

Connie Smith couldn't rightly remember just what had caused them to drift apart. It was one of those misunderstandings which were never cleared up, and when Robert was promoted and they'd moved away, the two women were still estranged.

That was over twenty years ago, and Connie often wished she could become friends with Myrtle again, who was now, like herself, a widow.

When Isla returned to the bungalow one evening about a week before the great occasion, she was completely unprepared for the sight which met her eyes when she opened the door of the living-room.

Mrs Smith was seated by the fire, her knitting in her hands, and a bandaged foot on a low footstool.

"My goodness!" Isla exclaimed. "Whatever happened?"

To her consternation, Mrs Smith burst into tears.

"Oh, Isla, it was so easily done," she sobbed. "I took Lassie out on her lead and Mrs Moncrieff's spaniel rushed at her. My foot got entangled with the lead and I just clattered down. I've sprained my ankle, fortunately it's not broken, but the doctor says I'll never be able to drive all that distance to Lochside."

"But how did you manage to get home, call the doctor and prepare the tea?" Isla asked.

"Mrs Cameron next door saw the accident. Oh, she was so kind. She brought me home and saw to everything."

"But you'll simply have to go to the reunion, somehow or other."

There was silence for a moment.

"I'll manage somehow," Mrs Smith said at last. "I'll take a taxi to the station, and the train as far as I can. Unfortunately, there's no line to Lochside now, so I expect I'll need to find out about a bus. That might involve another taxi to the bus station."

Isla looked at the brave little figure. There was no question of not going. Perhaps Norman could help out.

ISLA and Norman were going out the following evening, and over their meal she broached the subject of Mrs Smith and her reunion dinner. She wasn't too sure of his reaction, for sometimes Norman, though charming, could be quite unpredictable.

Not like her father, who'd have moved heaven and earth to get Mrs Smith to Lochside on time.

"Mrs Smith, your landlady?" Norman was saying. "She's hurt her ankle? Oh, that's a pity."

"It's a tragedy, as far as she's concerned." Isla told him how much she'd been looking forward to going. "The doctor says she couldn't possibly drive all that distance, and she's talking of going by taxi, train, taxi and bus.

"Norman." She hesitated nervously. "I do hope you don't mind me asking you, but do you think you could possibly take her?"

"When is this reunion?" he asked, without any great enthusiasm.

"The last Friday in November."

"But, Isla, that's the staff dance. Had you forgotten?"

"Of course," Isla said, deflated.

"If she's as keen as you say," Norman said, smoothly reasonable, "I've no doubt she'll make it with her taxi, train and bus."

"I wouldn't dream of letting her," Isla said spiritedly. "I'll drive her myself if she'll let me. It's ages since I've driven, but if I get in some practice it should be all right. I'll ask Mr Simpson tomorrow if I can get away a little earlier to take her."

"Don't be ridiculous! He won't want to let you off that day. We'll all be working like mad to get finished for the dance."

"I don't think Mr Simpson'll mind when he knows it's for Mrs Smith," Isla said shortly.

"For goodness sake! Of what importance is your landlady to the boss!" Norman sneered.

"Just the widow of the former manager. Mr Simpson and his wife are very fond of her," Isla said scathingly.

Norman's expression changed completely.

"Oh, is she that Mrs Smith? I didn't connect the name at all." Isla looked down at her plate, her cheeks burning angrily. She could almost hear him thinking that even if it meant missing the dance, it would be worth it to gain Mr Simpson's favour.

"Well, I suppose I could take her," he began casually.

Isla felt as if the last spoonful of the sweet would choke her.

" No, thank you," she said as politely as possible. " I'd hate you to miss the dance. I'm sure Mrs Smith and I will make it if we leave in plenty of time."

WHEN Isla suggested she drive her landlady to Lochside, Mrs Smith flushed with pleasure.

" If you don't mind trusting yourself with me. I'll practise with your car if you don't mind and I'm sure Mr Simpson will let me off early, so we could take plenty of time."

" Of course I'd much rather trust myself with you than make that long, difficult journey myself."

" For Mrs Smith, anything," Mr Simpson agreed when Isla put her plan to him.

Mrs Smith was looking pretty on the afternoon they set off for Lochside.

Isla drove well, and they made such good time that they decided to stop for afternoon tea.

The traffic was slightly heavier when they resumed their journey, and in a small town a few miles farther on they found themselves following a small fire tender, obviously owned by an industrial firm. They were moving quite slowly when the tender's indicator blinked to the left.

" Is it clear ahead ?" Mrs Smith asked.

" Yes, perfectly clear."

" Right. You can overtake, then."

Isla started to obey her instructions, but as she drew alongside the tender, it unexpectedly turned to the right and into their car, bumping along from wing to wing on the passenger side.

" Oh, what's happened ?" she cried in alarm.

" You're all right," Mrs Smith reassured her. " Just drive over to the left and draw up."

Her quiet voice calmed the girl, who did as she was told. As they came out of the car, they noticed the tender's indicator was still blinking to the left.

The teenage boy who'd been driving and another young man, probably in his mid twenties, came out of the vehicle together.

" Whatever made you do that ?" the older man asked unbelievingly.

" Because you indicated you were turning left." Mrs Smith pointed to the still-flashing indicator.

" Oh, I'm sorry," said the boy who'd been driving. " I thought I'd indicated right, and we have the type of indicator which doesn't flash inside the vehicle which way we're going."

Isla, who'd been standing listening to the conversation, suddenly found that she was shaking uncontrollably.

" Go into the car, dear," Connie Smith told her. " You'll be better there."

But when Isla tried to get in the passenger door, she found it jammed and had to go round to the other side where she sat in the driving seat, shivering and shaking in turn.

Outside, Mrs Smith leaned against the car, trying to keep the weight off her injured foot while the older of the men telephoned the police.

As they waited for them to come, the others got into the car because a drizzle of rain had started. Brian, the boy who'd been driving the tender, looked guilty and upset and Isla felt sorry for him.

" Where were you making for ?" asked the other man, who introduced himself as David Hamilton.

" Lochside. It's about forty miles away," Mrs Smith said.

" Yes, I've heard of it. That's quite some distance yet to go."

" Yes, we were supposed to be there about seven o'clock but," and she cast a quick glance at Isla's white face, " I'm afraid we'll just have to cancel it now. I think Isla's had too much of a shock to go on."

The police arrived at that moment, and as they got out of the car, David Hamilton leaned towards Isla and whispered urgently.

" Was it very important to get to Lochside tonight ?"

" Yes, very," Isla whispered back.

After the police had closed their notebooks and gone, and the car was found fit to drive, David Hamilton made a suggestion.

" I've been thinking, ladies, that I could drive you for the rest of your journey. I'm sure my boss would agree, under the circumstances."

" That's very kind of you, but I couldn't possibly . . ." Connie Smith began politely, but Isla silenced her gently.

" I think maybe you should consider accepting his offer, for neither of us can drive, and you're going to be very disappointed if you don't reach Lochside tonight after coming this far."

" I think that's a good idea, David." Brian spoke up unexpectedly. " I'd be much happier if I knew I hadn't spoilt everything for them."

Mrs Smith and Isla looked delightedly at each other.

" I really don't know what to say," the elder woman began, and David smiled.

" Then don't say anything at all. Just pop into the café for a cup of tea while I contact my boss and tell him what's happened. I was actually just getting a lift from one factory to another and he'll be wondering what's happened to me. Then I'll have to telephone my mother and tell her I won't be home until later."

" I don't know when I've met two nicer boys," Mrs Smith told Isla as they sat over their tea. " They're both so good-looking, too."

" Really ?" Isla said, sipping her tea.

" Don't tell me you didn't notice !"

The girl smiled shamefacedly.

" I was much too upset and worried about your car."

" Nonsense, it wasn't your fault. The important thing is that nobody's hurt."

As David Hamilton drove them to Lochside, Isla had time to study him and realise what Mrs Smith had said was true.

THEY reached Lochside in good time and left an excited Mrs Smith at the front door of the Lochside Arms.

Isla smiled affectionately as they watched the little figure make its way up the broad steps of the hotel.

" She's been so looking forward to this evening, it would have been a catastrophe if she'd missed it. It was so good of you bringing us here."
" Not at all. Anyone would have done the same."
Anyone wouldn't, you know, Isla thought privately, smiling at him. David leaned back in the driving seat and stretched his long legs.
" Well, what are we to do while Mrs Smith is enjoying herself ? I noticed another hotel on the way in. Why don't we have a meal there ?"
It was a modern place with murals of the Highlands and, over the meal, Isla learned that David had graduated from Glasgow University just two years ago, and had been employed by this firm ever since. He in turn heard about her job at the bank and how happy she was living with Mrs Smith. As they sat talking together, she began to believe there was something in the old adage about an ill wind blowing nobody good, and the staff dance seemed very far away.

MEANWHILE, Mrs Smith had taken off her coat and made her way to the room where the reunion was being held. An elderly woman who'd been watching her progress came over to her, smiling a welcome.
" Connie ! I'm so glad you were able to come. Mrs Young told me she'd had a letter from you, so I knew to look out for you."
It was Mrs Cunningham who'd been Commissioner in Mrs Smith's day and she was delighted to see her, as they'd always been good friends.
They were standing laughing at memories of the old days when they heard a quiet voice behind them.
" Hello, Connie. Welcome back."
It was Myrtle.
Connie turned quickly, then the two old friends took each other's hands and stood smiling at each other, tears not far away.
Just then they were joined by Margaret Leslie, who'd been one of their Brownies and gone on to become an officer herself.
" Come over and look at yourselves on some of the old photographs," she said after welcoming them, and there they were, so much younger looking and slimmer, but still the same Connie and Myrtle, surrounded by laughing Brownies.
By then it was time to sit down to the meal, and to her delight Connie found she was between Myrtle and Margaret.
Their very first Commissioner, Lady Carmichael of Green Braes, who was now an old, frail, but still remarkably attractive lady, was there to make the first speech of the evening. She reminded them of the inauguration of the Guides, their trials, tribulations and hilarious moments of fifty years ago.
She was followed by the first Captain of the 2nd Company, who had everyone wiping away tears of laughter at her amusing account of the time the charabanc taking the Guides to camp in Glen Clova broke down, and every piece of equipment had to be transferred, piece by piece, on to a farm cart. This done, the girls burst into song, only to frighten the horse which bolted, scattering the laboriously loaded equipment in its wake.
After this lady came the Brown Owl of the 1st Pack, who read out

the names of all the original Brownies present, and as one middle-aged lady after another stood up, smiling, the applause became more and more enthusiastic.

BY the end of the evening, a tired but happy Connie Smith had shaken hands with everyone there, had giggled at happy memories and felt sad, when asking about some, to find life had treated them badly. But best of all was seeing Myrtle again, and they parted with the promise that Myrtle would visit her old friend soon for a little holiday.

Isla and David were waiting outside in the car.

Mrs Smith was delighted to see them, slipping into the back of the car and talking non-stop for almost an hour.

When at last she'd spoken herself to a halt, she asked what they'd done with themselves all evening and was delighted to hear they'd accidentally chosen the hotel where her wedding reception had been held, forty-one years ago.

As they drew near to the town where David lived, the thought which had been niggling at the back of Isla's mind all evening suddenly loomed very large indeed. She'd need to drive home the rest of the way. But apparently this wasn't David's plan at all.

" I wouldn't be happy thinking of the two of you making your way home at this late hour," he said. " Just let me telephone Mother again from the next box. It would take too long to go to my house."

Mrs Smith began to say she was sure she could drive but as she did, the light from a street lamp fell on his face as he looked at his fellow passenger in the front, and when she saw his expression she smiled to herself and decided to say nothing. While he was telephoning, she leaned over and spoke quickly to Isla.

" Should I ask him to stay overnight ? How is he to get back otherwise ? There are no buses as late as this."

Not surprisingly, Isla thought this a wonderful idea . . .

Peace and a contented mind follow you to this bay.

BECAUSE it was winter time, two days before Christmas, and because nobody ever visited Achnacarraig in winter, Helen Ferguson had the dining-room of the small hotel all to herself at breakfast.

Mrs Thomson, the brisk young landlady, sounded almost apologetic as she made sure everything was to her guest's liking.

"You see," she explained, "we've no central heating or the like. We don't even keep a girl on in winter since there's nothing in Achnacarraig but the fishing, and nobody ever dreams of coming here in winter, most especially Americans!"

"All the kinder of you to put yourself out to make things so nice for me," Helen returned. "But I'm not American really, I was born in Achnacarraig."

The landlady, giving the cut glass marmalade dish a final shine, raised her thin eyebrows in surprise.

72

Where Yesterday Meets
—— Today ——

by Mairi Munro

"Born?" she repeated. "In Achnacarraig! Just fancy that now! Well, I suppose you'll notice a few changes in the place!"

"After thirty years?" Helen laughed lightly. "I suppose I will, really. I hadn't thought about that. Of course, it was dark when I came in last night so I haven't really seen anything yet."

"Maybe," the landlady placed the knitted cosy over the squat teapot, "maybe you should've come in summer instead."

Helen nodded in vague agreement. From outside, as someone opened a door, came the momentary winter song of the burn running beneath the old bridge with the white, curving parapet, just across the road.

Sometimes, when the frost came hard, icicles had used to hang from the arch like long spears of bright glass; on the way to school, the boys used to crunch down through the frost-glittering dead leaves and break those spears off, handing them up to the girls who squealed from the sudden shock of the icicles grasped by fingers already red from the frozen air of the morning.

Once Andrew Chisholm had given Helen charge of the very biggest, brightest icicle ever seen, and she had let it fall from her frozen hands to break in pieces on the hard road; and she had burst into tears and run ahead of all the others up the brae to the school, not because of the icicle but because of Andrew who had given it into her care.

Helen had stayed miserable and tearful all morning. Then at playtime, Andrew had lent her his handkerchief and besides that, had given her the core of his apple, not eaten right down either, but with a full, luscious, tooth-long bite left on it all round. Daisy Lyle had tossed her flaxen head scornfully and flourished her own unblemished cambric hankie with a show of independence, yet she was quite unable to hide from Helen's now brighter eyes the fact that Daisy would have given the warm rabbit fur mittens from off her hands, for just one bite of Andrew Chisholm's apple.

" Winter's so dead in Achnacarraig," Mrs Thomson spoke softly.

" I beg your pardon?" The outside door closed, the song of the burn was cut off, and Helen leapt back out of the depth of years. " Dead? Oh, yes, I see what you mean."

And the word fell with flat heaviness on to the carpeted floor of the cosy dining-room.

LEFT alone, Helen chewed her toast thoughtfully, looking out through the hotel window to where the late-rising sun just touched the tip of Ben Bhan, snow streaked in the deep gullies. That band of gold would widen slowly, till it flooded the glen, lighting the hoar-laden tips of the pine trees on the school brae with a million bright candles; but for a short time only, since she knew how the icicles beneath the arch used to freeze again even as a melting drip prepared to part, leaving the gleaming blades even longer than before.

Maybe this stranger was right; this landlady who was from outside and could look at Achnacarraig with eyes undazzled with the stars of memory. Maybe she should have left her visit till summer, or never come at all.

Madge Peterson, Helen's flat-mate in Denver, Colorado, had said she was plain crazy. But then, what did Madge have for memories? Sunshine and the waving grasses of Alabama? You got to know people's memories by the way they talked, and Madge talked of nothing but sunshine.

For over thirty years in towns and cities of the United States, Helen's own memories of Achnacarraig had been of winter and Christmas-time, of roaring fires in the chimney, of frozen ponds and frost-glittering pine, of boots ringing on hard stone roads beneath skies shaking with stars and of ankle-deep rustling leaves on the path through the beechwood to where stood the clump of holly trees, brightly red with clustering berries.

It was such memories that had drawn her nearly four thousand miles to be here, just at this time. An impulse perhaps, maybe not unrelated to that other impulse that thirty years ago and at Christmas-time, too, had set the feet of the twenty-year-old girl she then was on her way across a still war-torn Atlantic.

Plain crazy? Helen crumbled the last of the toast on to her plate. Maybe. But, crazy or not, here she was.

CONTRARY to Mrs Thomson's warning, Helen didn't find Achnacarraig as changed as even she herself might have expected.

True, the tiny shop of her schooldays was now twice the size with wide display windows and a young couple with Border accents presided briskly where once Miss MacKay had counted sweets, slowly, into skilfully twisted cones of paper. It used to be awful if the school bell went while Miss MacKay was still meticulously tucking down the broad end of the conical poke and asking after your grandma's rheumatism and telling you what a big girl you were growing, and why didn't you tie your hair up in neat plaits like Daisy Lyle always did?

Helen found herself laughing aloud, to the astonishment of a glossy, yellow-beaked blackbird busily harvesting the winter berries from the cotoneaster along the hedge.

The school had closed for the holidays but, passing by, Helen could see the star-topped tip of the Christmas tree, standing just as it always had, in the corner by the window.

Looking at it there, Helen had a strange momentary feeling of being something like the Sleeping Beauty of the fairy tale, who woke up after a long time to find everything going ahead exactly where she had left off.

Mightn't that be the very same tree, the selfsame tinselled star, standing just where she had helped to decorate it for the Christmas party of thirty years ago? A party still waiting, since Helen hadn't gone to it that year but had, instead, left for Glasgow on the long road that hadn't known her returning steps till now.

Decorating the tree and the school itself had been tremendous fun that year. The recently appointed infant mistress, Bessie Shearer, had asked Donny Cameron, who worked in his father's joinery shop, to come along and help. Bob Chisholm had gone along with Donny, since whatever the one did, the other was never far away. Andrew had gone with his younger brother, naturally, and had taken Helen as well as Daisy Lyle along; to hold things, as they'd said. Donny had been glad enough to have them all there. It was clear he hadn't quite made up his mind about Bessie, though everybody else knew Bessie's own mind had been firmly made up since they'd both been five years old.

Helen knew those two had married, and were probably grandparents by now. She had got news of them, as well as of others, only once when, ten years ago at a St Andrew's Night dinner in New York City, she had found herself sitting next to a burly sea captain whose ship chanced to be in the harbour at the time. She had recognised her companion instantly and joyfully as Calum Black, whom the dominie had always designated dunce of their class.

Beyond the church, the wandering road wound downwards towards the loch, from where the joyous shouts of children rose now on the clear air.

With a smile for a robin, Helen walked briskly on, knowing of a certainty what was going on down there. On a reed-encircled pond just above the gravelly shore, children had made a slide on the ice, and were sliding singly, in pairs and in long rows, brightly-coloured scarves streaming out behind them, ecstatic squeals and shouts rending the winter stillness.

Watching those children now was like standing aside and seeing herself and those others who had been young then, too, on that particular Christmas-time when they had realised that, before another Christmas came round, they would all have left the village school and some of them the village itself.

It had all come true. They had all gone their several ways. Bob and Andrew Chisholm to High School and the Agricultural College; Bessie Shearer and Daisy Lyle to school in Edinburgh, Donny Cameron to his father's workshop, Helen herself to train as a children's nurse, and Calum Black to start his apprenticeship on his uncle's cargo vessel.

Never again were they to be as those joyous children down there now, sliding, tumbling and getting up again.

Never again, indeed, had they found themselves all together in Achnacarraig save for that one last time when Helen, at twenty, had stayed on alone at the cottage after her grandmother's death, and they had gathered together to set up and decorate the Christmas tree which Helen had, moments ago, so strangely felt to be the very tree that had stood there, ever since.

" It's good to be together again, Helen," Andrew had said simply.

" Yes, Andrew, it's good. Just like old times."

" Old times," he had repeated, softly. " But there's new times ahead, Helen. This war has to end, soon. Have you thought of what you might want to do? I know you like your job, but Glasgow's such a way off. Have you ever thought you might like to come home to Achnacarraig for good?"

HELEN had been glad of the soft dark that hid the deep longing in her eyes. Home to Achnacarraig. Home.

" I don't know," Helen pondered. " You know that ambassador's wife I told you of? Their tour of duty's up, they're going back to America soon and trying hard to get me to go with the children. I didn't promise nor refuse outright. Anyway, I had to come home to clear up at Grandma's cottage. I got that job finished today. It's pretty bare, I can tell you. I hadn't the heart to put up even one sprig of holly!"

" Holly!" Andrew had stopped in the dark. " Helen, I'm glad you reminded me! Didn't I promise to get some for old Miss MacKay?

" Helen, I'll have to get that holly tomorrow afternoon. I'll come down from the top, the farm end. Will you take the path up the beechwood, to where the hollies stand, you remember the place? There's something I want to tell you, Helen. Can you meet me there about three?"

Deep in her memories, Helen hadn't till now noticed that the voices of the children down at the pond had died into silence, that the children themselves had gone.

There, unchanged in its faded green paint, was the little gate leading into the path up through the leafless winter beechwood, to where the holly trees must still stand.

But Helen didn't loose the catch, nor push the gate open. The moment of dream-excitement passed as quickly as it had come, leaving her knees strangely weak; telling her, as she ought to have known before now, that she shouldn't ever have given way to the impulse that had carried her to this spot.

Oh, it had been different, then. As though it had been yesterday, Helen remembered the crinkling rustle of the dead leaves on the path and saw herself in her red-hooded cape walking lightly up towards the clearing where the holly trees grew.

Andrew had his back towards her as Helen had stepped lightly from the pathway to the edge of the clearing. In his strong arms he held the slim, willowy form of Daisy Lyle, who leaned far back, her blue eyes closed, her flaxen hair cascading over the shoulders of her fur-lined cape.

Oh, Andrew! Andrew! Was it to tell me this you asked me here to meet you? I who have loved you since we rolled as infants on the green by the burn.

Never afterwards could Helen remember clearly her breathless running down the path she had so lightly come up.

That had all been thirty years ago. Helen had caught the bus for Glasgow within the next hour, without saying goodbye to anyone save old Miss MacKay, in whose shop she had sought shelter till the bus came.

Even so, twenty years later, Andrew's was the first name to come crowding from heart to lips that night she had met Captain Calum Black.

She hadn't been able to ask him outright. Instead, she had gone round everything in a complicated way, coming finally to the part she had to know.

"And tell me, Calum, do you remember Daisy Lyle, Daisy Chisholm as she is now, of course? You know, Calum, I used to think you had a fancy for Daisy yourself!"

"I . . . I see Daisy a bit," he had admitted, almost awkwardly. "I don't believe I mentioned, but likely you'll know, that she's been a widow this five years or so back.

"She's got one boy, about ten years old, I reckon. I'd never been home much, as you'll know. Then, about a month back, I gave this youngster a lift from the school. I didn't have to ask his name, I can tell you that. You'll remember Andrew? Well, this was a living copy of Andrew Chisholm at that age, sitting there beside me. I took him home, and Daisy asked me to stay to tea. She's a fine woman, Daisy."

THERE ahead was the opening to the clearing where the holly trees were, the place where Andrew would be waiting for her.

And there he was, leaning carelessly against the broad bole of a tree, his dark hair thrown back carelessly as always and his brown eyes lit with all the fun and joy of being twenty.

Long days after this moment, Helen tried without success to remember if she had cried out as she felt the blood drain from her face.

All she can recall is waking to the half-dream reality of two strong arms about her, and her eyes looking upward into the face of the boy who had waited for thirty long years at this spot.

"Andrew!" she breathed.

The young man's eyes wrinkled questioningly.

"Are you all right? I didn't mean to startle you, standing there. But how do you come to know my name?"

"I didn't really know your name was Andrew," she explained weakly. "But I thought it must be. I think I knew your parents rather long ago, when they were about your age."

"My dad's dead," the boy said quietly, and Helen nodded.

"I heard that," she said. "In New York City of all places, from Captain Black. You are very, very like your dad," she added, her eyes searching his face with hungry memory.

"I was barely five when he died," he said. "So I don't remember him very well. Yet everybody says I'm very like Uncle Andrew, whom I was named after!"

"Your Uncle Andrew?" she repeated, in a very low voice. "That idiot, Calum Black! He never told me . . . oh, no wonder he was always the dunce of the class!"

"Was my step-dad really a dunce?" he asked delightedly. "He says he was, but Mum doesn't agree at all!"

Before Helen could reply to a question there was really no way of answering, a twig broke in the holly clearing behind them and they both looked round.

" Helen !"

The man who stood there had white hair that had once been dark, and a face lined by time and weather.

" Andrew!" Helen walked towards him, steadily now, and he took both her hands in his.

YOU'LL never believe this, Helen," Andrew said at last. " I haven't been in here for years and years. Funny thing, I was waiting for a girl, that time. And Daisy came down the path that day. She must have run too fast, I suppose, for she took some sort of a fainting attack and I had the dickens of a job bringing her round. In the end, I had to carry her up to the house, and leave her with my mother."

Neither said anything for a long time. Both knew there was much to say, a long gap to fill. Yet, standing there in the holly clearing where they had trysted to meet thirty years earlier, neither felt the need for words.

In the end, Helen was the first to speak.

" The holly is lovely," she remarked.

Andrew looked up sharply.

" Holly!" He slapped his knee, as he'd done in the dark above the bridge, long ago. " Helen, I'm glad you reminded me! Didn't I promise to get some for the young people at the shop and, like the idiot I am, I forgot!"

At his words, the years rolled away as if they had never been. They were back to that evening when, after decorating the tree, they had walked down the brae together and Bob and Daisy had run ahead.

They both knew the words that should come next.

" Helen," Andrew said, " I'll get that holly tomorrow."

" I'll help you gather it," Helen rejoined. " And this time . . . this time I really will!"

A walk at twilight by the gentle loch.

79

LOVE CAME DOWN AT CHRISTMAS

BY MARGARET NICOL

IT was going to be the best Christmas ever.

Case in hand, Cathy Dunbar made her way into the Central Station to catch the train for home. Many people were doing the same on this Christmas Eve, but few could have felt the same thrill of anticipation.

It was Christmas and she was going home to the manse at Holmlea, but that wasn't the only reason. Someone who meant the whole world to her was coming too. Roger Martin, the young accountant whom she had met at an office dance, was to meet her on the platform.

Lately, Cathy's letters home had been full of Roger ; she simply could not keep him out of them. Her mother had written back, somewhat doubtfully.

Love Came Down At Christmas

He seems a nice boy, Cathy, but ought you to build yourself up like this? You take things so much to heart, I wouldn't like you to to be hurt. Of course he can come to stay over Christmas, but you know how quietly we live . . . I hope he understands.

Of course Roger understood! His own home was much gayer, it was true. Cathy had been invited there and had felt a little lost in the suburban villa with his teenage sisters and bright, society mother. She had never met his father, for he had been in hospital for a long time, but Roger always spoke of him in a tender, loving way that betrayed his fondness for him. That same note had crept into his voice lately when he and Cathy said goodbye after a happy time together. Yes, he was fond of her, she knew, but did he feel this wild, hungry longing that beat in her own heart day and night?

The train was standing at the platform, but Cathy wouldn't board it till Roger arrived. She put down her case and tidied back her long, fair hair, her eyes on the approaching passengers. Ah, there he was, on time as usual. She waved and smiled, and Roger waved back, but he wasn't smiling. As he hurried towards her, she noticed that he wasn't carrying a case.

" Roger, is there anything wrong?" she asked anxiously.

" Not exactly wrong, Cathy, but I can't come to Holmlea with you."

" Oh, Roger, you might have told me before this!"

" I couldn't," he replied. " We've just had word that Dad is to get home from hospital in the morning and I've got to be there to help."

" Is it so necessary?" she stammered.

" Yes, it is. I thought you would understand, Cathy."

Roger couldn't possibly know what this meant to her, after all her rosy dreams.

" Well, I suppose it can't be helped. I . . . I hope you have a happy Christmas."

The whistle sounded and he grabbed her case.

" Come, I'll see you into a seat."

At last they found an empty seat and he put her case in the rack.

" So long then, Cathy! If I can, I'll phone you tomorrow about five."

CATHY sat as if stunned in her corner, her big handbag on her knee. It was stupid to cry, but she couldn't help it. When no one was looking, she snatched up her hanky to wipe her eyes.

Yes, it was going to be a hateful Christmas. No doubt Roger was right to stay and support his father and she admired him for doing so, but that didn't make it any easier to bear and no doubt he was as disappointed as she was, though perhaps . . . if he wasn't serious about her, the prospect of meeting her family might have been too much.

And now she would have to face the family and village by herself, admitting that her boy friend wasn't coming after all. Some of them might even think that Roger was just a figment of her imagination. It was going to be absolutely unendurable.

Cathy's eyes were still red when she got out of the train at Holmlea. She knew she looked terrible, but for once she didn't care. What did

81

it matter how she looked? To cover up her misery was beyond her, though she did try to smile when she saw her father and brother Paul on the platform.

With a few bounds Paul reached her side.

" Where's the boy friend ?" he asked, taking her case. " I thought he was coming back with you."

" So did I," she replied shortly. " He was unavoidably detained."

" You mean he chickened out at the last minute ?"

" No such thing !"

She turned to her tall, smiling father.

" All alone ?" he asked.

" Yes, Dad." Shakily she explained the reason for Roger's absence.

THEY got into the ancient manse car at the station gate and reached the house all too soon. It was the moment Cathy dreaded. They seemed to pass the whole of Holmlea on the way and they were all intent on having a peep at the boy friend, Cathy was sure. Now it would soon be round the place that there wasn't one at all. Yet she would have to confront them all tomorrow at church . . . Perhaps she could pretend to be ill and miss the service ?

She kissed her mother who, of course, put the inevitable question. It was her father who explained, while her two aunts twittered away beside him.

Aunt Betsy, tall and thin with big features who referred to herself as a " bachelor girl," laughed coyly.

" There you are, you see. Men were deceivers ever !"

Aunt Hilda, who was a widow and dressed in colourful style with lots of beads, couldn't look gloomy if she tried. She took Cathy's arm chummily.

" We'll just have to do our best to cheer you up !" She laughed her big, happy laugh, but Cathy pulled her arm away and ran quickly upstairs.

As she sat on her bed nursing her resentment, Cathy reflected how thoughtless and heartless the older generation were ! Because she was young, they thought she couldn't feel. True, her father had been sympathetic, but he was a special kind of person, for in his profession he was obliged to be kind and good.

Time passed and she was still waiting there when her mother came in. She looked fussed and anxious.

" Cathy, what's keeping you ? Tea's ready. Aren't you going to change ?"

" I can't be bothered," was the listless response. " Would it matter very much if I didn't come down ?"

" Of course it would matter !" Mrs Dunbar's voice was a little sharp.

" Well, if I do come, I shan't be very good company."

" Oh, Cathy, do try ! If you feel bad, that's no reason to cast a cloud over all the company."

" How can you expect me to be bright and gay after what's happened ?" she demanded. " I'll come down for tea if you like, but I don't feel in the least hungry."

Love Came Down At Christmas

After her mother had gone, Cathy had the grace to feel ashamed. Poor Mum, she deserved better, but that black mood which had gripped her wouldn't be shaken off. After combing her hair and powdering her nose she appeared in the dining-room just as the meal started.

After tea, the others gathered in the sitting-room beside the piano and she joined them there. There was a little silver Christmas tree with lights at the window, and holly was tucked round the picture frames. A sprig of mistletoe hung from the middle light, but what good was mistletoe now? All the lights in the room were on. Such extravagance only happened at Christmas, and everything looked very gay.

Except Cathy's face, of course.

"Come on, folks, let's make the welkin ring!"

Mr and Mrs Dunbar took it in good part and joined heartily in the old songs, but Cathy didn't sing a note.

Where did her aunts get their high spirits from? Probably they'd had things easy all their lives with no hardships or disappointments; they'd had all the ups of life without any of the downs.

Cathy had taken up an old photo album which was always put out at Christmas. It showed a lot of old-fashioned pictures of her relatives in their youth and usually she had a good laugh when she turned the pages, but tonight she couldn't summon up even a small giggle and closed the book in disgust.

> ## RADIANCE
>
> *There are three looks upon a woman's*
> *   face*
> *That bring to her a rare and lovely*
> *   grace—*
> *The wondering innocence when first*
> *   she sees*
> *What love can mean; its sweet*
> *   felicities.*
>
> *And next, the look that every bride*
> *   should wear,*
> *Meeting her bridegroom who is wait-*
> *   ing there—*
> *The trustful gaze which holds no hint*
> *   of fear,*
> *But simply says, ' I'll love you*
> *   always, dear!'*
>
> *And last, that look of mother-love*
> *   complete,*
> *Humble before the miracle most sweet:*
> *The look that whispers, 'Darling*
> *   child of mine,*
> *Here of God's loving is the proof and*
> *   sign!'*
>
> CLAIRE RITCHIE

Now they were singing "Love's Old Sweet Song" with sentimental relish. It was too much and Cathy sprang to her feet.

"Goodnight, everybody! I'm off to bed."

IN bed a short time later, Cathy found she couldn't sleep. The aunts were playing a duet now which they performed every Christmas and even with the blankets over her head she could hear it.

But the music stopped at last and there were sounds of feet on the stair and goodnights being said. Then all was quiet, but still Cathy lay awake.

" I can't sleep and that's that."

Slipping on her dressing-gown she crept downstairs. At least she could make herself a cup of tea.

To her surprise the sitting-room light was still on. Had they forgotten to put it out ? Peeping in, she saw her father there on the sofa, his greying head bent over the photo album she had discarded. He looked up in surprise.

" Cathy ! Is anything the matter ?"

" I just couldn't sleep. I thought everyone was in bed."

" I ought to be, but I started looking at these old photos. Fascinating !"

She sat down beside him to look. It was peaceful in here and having him to herself was something which seldom happened. Her eye lit on a picture of Aunt Betsy in her twenties, wearing a very long tweed skirt and tailored blouse, her hair caught back in a bun.

" I'd know her anywhere, she hasn't changed. Why did she never marry, Dad ?"

" It's a sad story," he replied. " When this picture was taken, Betsy was actually engaged. Look, there's her ring."

" Well !" exclaimed Cathy. " What happened ?"

" I was only a boy at the time, but I remember it well," he told her. " Everything was ready for the wedding. The day had dawned, but the bridegroom never turned up."

" How awful for her," breathed Cathy.

" Yes, I'll never forget that night. My room was next to Betsy's and I heard her crying. It went on all night, heartbroken sobbing. Yet next day she was Betsy again, the bright girl we knew, and has been ever since."

CATHY swallowed.

" I wonder how she did it. I couldn't have."

" Betsy is strong-minded," observed her father. " She has her faults . . . tactlessness for instance . . . but loading her grief on others is not one of them."

" I somehow thought she'd never had any grief, that she'd got off lightly."

" Very few people get off lightly," was the reply. " Yet some of our brightest souls are the ones who have suffered most."

She turned over a page and there was a youthful Aunt Hilda with a handsome man she'd been told was her Uncle James.

" I suppose Aunt Hilda had her bad times, too."

" She certainly had. James was killed in the last war."

" Oh, Dad, what a selfish beast I am !"

He smiled.

" I hadn't noticed it. Anyhow, there's plenty of time to remedy it. Tomorrow's Christmas. Peace on earth, goodwill towards men."

" Goodwill," mused his daughter. " I haven't shown much of that tonight, have I ? But I'll make amends."

In bed, Cathy settled down peacefully.

" Tomorrow I'll show a different face," she vowed. " Even if I don't feel happy, I'll pretend to be. Here I've been moaning because

I've to do without Roger for a day or two, while the aunts have lost the ones they loved for ever."

Laden with parcels, she went downstairs the following morning. Everybody was up and the present giving had started.

"A Merry Christmas!" she called from the door and they all looked round, faces wreathed in smiles. She went round the table kissing everyone as she handed out her parcels, giving an extra hug to the aunts. She didn't need to pretend she was happy, it was how she really felt.

There was a big rush to get ready for church. Cathy's idea of feigning illness seemed ridiculous now. In the quiet building with the organist playing, she felt strangely peaceful and she joined in the carols with all her old fervour. When her father read out the wonderful Christmas story, the message of it struck her more meaningfully than ever before.

Glory to God in the Highest and on earth peace and goodwill toward men.

Like most people, Cathy was continually puzzled and saddened by the confusion and wickedness in the world, yet felt helpless to do anything about it. She was only one tiny unit of humanity, yet wasn't humanity made up of tiny units? If everybody tried to give goodwill surely the world would be a better place? It was what her father believed and she felt sure he was right.

After the church service people came up to wish her a happy Christmas and she felt her heart going out to them. They didn't seem to notice the absence of her boy friend after all, but even if they had she wouldn't have been annoyed, or at least she wouldn't have shown it. Probably all these friends who were smiling and wishing her well had their secret sadnesses which they were covering up. If they could do it, so could she.

A S was their habit, the aunts got ready for an afternoon walk to get an appetite for the big meal.

"Coming with us, Cathy?"

They asked that every Christmas and she always made some excuse, but today was different.

"Well, I'm expecting a phone call at five, but we could be back long before that. I'll come. In fact, I'd love to."

What happened next wasn't in the day's programme. Aunt Hilda wore shoes with high heels and wasn't looking where she was going. Suddenly her foot twisted on the rough path and she came down in a heap.

At first she took it as a joke and laughed as Aunt Betsy and Cathy pulled her up. But she flopped down again as soon as they let her go.

"I've sprained my ankle, I think. How silly!"

"Never mind, we'll get home home all right," Cathy assured her.

"Weren't you expecting a message from your boy friend, Cathy?" Aunt Betsy said. "You'd better run on, you might be in time. Go on! I'll manage Hilda alone."

"Yes," Aunt Hilda urged, smiling in spite of pain."

"Nonsense, Auntie! I'm staying by you. If Roger rings he can just ring again." But would he? Might not the company at home be too absorbing ? Put the thought from you, Cathy, you've got to keep your spirits up and the aunts', too. And so they staggered on.

Fortunately the village hospital was on their way home, so they helped Hilda inside and a nurse took her along to have her ankle bandaged. Betsy said she would stay with her.

" You go home now and ask your father to bring the car for us."

Cathy ran, but by this time it was nearer six than five.

" What's happened ?" her mother asked anxiously. " And where are the others ?"

Cathy explained breathlessly.

" Can Dad fetch them in the car ? And, Mum, did Roger phone ?"

" Nobody phoned," was the reply. " Sorry, Cathy."

The door bell rang. Open it with a bright face and a welcoming smile, she told herself. Now, Cathy, show the Christmas spirit !

" Hello, Cathy ! Is it all right ? Can I come in ?"

" Roger !" She was breathless with delight.

" It's me all right. The train was held up, or I'd have been here at five. Once Dad was home and feeling fine, he insisted that I came. He's very understanding, you know."

" So is my father. Everybody is. I've got a great family. You'll have to meet the aunts, but unfortunately one of them has sprained her ankle. But that won't spoil the fun if I know Aunt Hilda !"

CATHY was right. Hilda's spirits weren't dimmed in the least and through the meal she was the life and soul of the party. As for Cathy, she sat in a happy trance smiling at everybody.

Later, they went out together for a stroll through the village. Christmas trees twinkled in the small cottage windows, and from the village hall came the sound of children singing *Away In A Manger.*

" It feels like Christmas here," Roger said. " More than it does in town."

His arm was round her and he turned up her face to his. In the pale light his eyes looked into hers for a long minute.

" What's different about you, Cathy ?"

" Perhaps I've found the Christmas spirit."

" Then please, dear, teach it to me. I love it and I love you. Shall we get married soon, Cathy ?"

" Yes, please," was her happy reply.

She knew the aunts would be delighted, and they were. Everybody stayed up very late, playing games and singing. The songs Cathy had scorned yesterday seemed very beautiful tonight, especially " Love's Old Sweet Song." It was the end of an unforgettable Christmas Day.

York is one of the most fascinating of English cities. Most visitors are eager to see the famous York Minster, and a leisurely walk along the medieval city walls, from which the view of the Minster is excellent, is a pleasant way to pass the time. There has been a settlement at York since Roman times when it was a garrison of great importance.

York

J. Campbell Kerr

KINLOCHARN'S NEW TEACHER

by Anne Murray

IT had been the busiest week Ruth Taylor had ever known. There had been that unexpected journey to Ross-shire, then back to Glasgow to pack up and tidy the flat where she had lived for some months. So many final things had to be done, but now all was in order and she had only to pay her visit to the convalescent home that afternoon.

Everything had happened so quickly. Was it only last Sunday evening that her uncle had phoned from his Inverness home? She had listened with keen interest as he explained how a Ross-shire friend of his had been telling him how impossible it seemed to find a suitable teacher for one small school.

" I remember you saying you hoped to get a country post again one of these days," he had gone on. " As you're just doing temporary work at present, I wondered what you would think about the Kinlocharn School."

Kinlocharn! Ruth's thoughts had flown back to a carefree teenage holiday at the youth hostel there, and how she had loved the district. She remembered the quiet little village close to the loch, and she hadn't forgotten the appearance of the schoolhouse, a low, one-storey building. It was the thought of the schoolhouse which made her decide to go there if the education committee would have her.

Yes, Kinlocharn was the very place for her in the circumstances. The people, too, she remembered as kind and helpful and friendly, and it was just such neighbours that she might well need in the immediate future, for she knew that the task which lay before her was not going to be easy.

So it was in a mood of mingled excitement and anxiety that she set off a few days later on the long, tiring journey north for her interview with the education committee. She knew that she was a good teacher and had little doubt that she could run the school at Kinlocharn, but so much depended on the coming meeting that it was not surprising that she felt apprehensive.

THE education committee were only too anxious to secure a well-qualified teacher, and one who had previously gained experience in a small country school. It had been a real crisis for them when the last teacher went off to get married and only temporary help could be found to replace her.

"Could you possibly start work next Monday, Miss Taylor?" the chairman had asked. "Perhaps you could manage, seeing you aren't in a settled post just now. If it's any help to you, there is quite a lot of furniture in the schoolhouse which you could have . . . quite nice stuff, too, left there by a former teacher for the use of any successor requiring it."

One of the lady members of the committee was looking rather doubtfully at Ruth's engagement ring.

"May I ask Miss Taylor if she intends to get married soon?" she inquired. "We don't want to have to keep on making changes."

Ruth felt it best to be candid.

"Marriage won't affect my work," she said quietly. "My fiancé was very badly hurt in a car accident, and it's on his account that I would like to settle in the country and make a home for him."

At that there were sympathetic murmurs and a general feeling that the Kinlocharn schoolhouse would be the very place for a young man confined to a wheelchair who wasn't likely to walk ever again.

Now, as she stood in the Glasgow flat looking down at the busy street far below, Ruth's dark eyes were tender while she thought of Mark Douglas. They had been engaged for a year, and while she worked in Perthshire and he in Glasgow they had met frequently.

If it hadn't been for his accident they would have been married by now. What a disaster that had been! One minute Mark was driving his car on the Perth motorway, the next crushed by the out-of-control lorry which had hurtled across the central reservation. It was a miracle he hadn't been killed.

Now, after weary months of hospital treatment, the final verdict had been given. No more could be done for him, and the injuries he'd received meant he wasn't likely ever to get back his power of walking. Apart from that, his general health was quite good.

Mark had taken it all bravely. Like Ruth, he was very much on his own. When he left the Glasgow hospital there was nowhere for him to go but the small convalescent home on the Ayrshire coast, and there Ruth had visited him as often as possible.

She hadn't hesitated over giving up her Perthshire work and taking temporary jobs in Glasgow so that she could be near him and could visit him as often as possible. Of course it had meant a considerable financial sacrifice on her part, for these temporary posts were not as well paid as her permanent post had been, but what was money compared with making Mark's new life as bearable as possible, and being with him often?

It was remarkable how well he had managed to keep his spirits up in spite of his misfortunes. But still, Ruth knew, there were times when, alone in his room, depression set in and he despaired of ever recapturing his past happiness.

Ruth had never had any doubts about going ahead with her plans to marry Mark in spite of his disability, but she sometimes suspected that he worried in case, in this new situation, she would prefer to terminate their relationship, and she was ever at pains to avoid giving him any evidence to support this theory. She loved Mark and wanted to marry him. His being unable to walk made not one whit of difference on that score.

TODAY was Saturday and she hadn't seen him since last Sunday afternoon. Had he wondered at her silence this week? Setting off to get her car from the garage, Ruth began to wish she hadn't kept the events of the week from him. Suddenly it didn't seem such a good idea after all to settle everything by herself, then spring it on him as a pleasant surprise.

Surely it would be just that? He would like to hear that they would soon be married and living together in a delightful corner of the West Highlands. Besides, it would be a splendid place to go on with his recent partially successful efforts at writing.

Oh, yes, he'd be thrilled. Ruth had convinced herself of this by the time she was turning in at the big gates and driving up the avenue which led to the house.

A few minutes later she was with him. Mark looked a lot better today, she decided with satisfaction.

" How have you been this week?" she asked as they kissed.

" Not bad at all," he replied. " You should see the speed I get out of my chair now when I go round the garden !"

" Mark, do be careful," she warned.

" Don't worry, darling, I will be. And I've got a job. What do you think of that?"

She stared in astonishment.

"A job?"

"Oh, nothing much. Doing secretarial work here, with a minute salary attached. It means I can stay on indefinitely."

Ruth breathed again. That arrangement wasn't a very important one. Now she must tell him her news.

"Mark, you remember I went once to a lovely place called Kinlocharn?"

"Up in Ross-shire? You spent a holiday there, didn't you?"

"Yes, before I knew you."

"And you nearly got drowned one day and were rescued by the postmistress whose name was MacLeod. Fancy my remembering that!" marvelled Mark. "I suppose it's because MacLeod was my mother's name as well."

"There wasn't any real danger of drowning," she pointed out. "I slipped off the side of the jetty and Miss MacLeod called me into the post office where she supplied hot soup and dry clothes. She was really most kind," Ruth recalled. "Well, Mark, you and I are going to live at Kinlocharn. What do you think about that?"

It was his turn to stare.

"I don't understand," he said bluntly.

HURRIEDLY, she explained. She mentioned the schoolhouse, so suitably built with no difficult steps anywhere, and described the sort of life they would lead.

"It'll be a good place for you to get on with your writing," she told him. "I'll come south the first possible weekend and we'll get married. Then I'll take you up there . . . in an ambulance, I think, so that the journey isn't too much for you. When I'm busy teaching I'll still be within call if you need me."

"And you support us both," said Mark evenly. "Two stories having been accepted isn't very far on the road to being a profitable writer."

Ruth's heart sank. She'd never heard him speak in that bitter tone. Worse was to follow.

"No, Ruth, that plan's out," said Mark firmly. "I've been thinking for some time that we ought to call off our marriage. Why should you be tied to a useless fellow like me? Since you've fixed up this new job you'll have to go to it and you'll be too far away to visit me often. It would be best to make the break now, for it's time you were free of me once and for all.

"I've had plenty of time to do a lot of thinking while I've been down here, Ruth, and I've come to one or two conclusions over the past couple of days. I'm likely to be like this for the rest of my life now. Do you realise what that would mean?"

He looked steadily at Ruth, and then continued.

"It means that you might always have to support me financially and look after me, doing all the things I can't do for myself. What sort of life would that be for you? How soon would you think of me as a burden which had ruined your whole life? No, Ruth, it wouldn't work.

You'd end up hating me instead of loving me and I couldn't stand that.

"It would be better if you went away now and forgot about me, and that we never see each other again."

RUTH sat speechless for a long moment. At last she got out a few whispered words.

"I . . . I thought you loved me, Mark."

"It's because I do that I won't spoil your life," he returned. "It's no life for a woman to be tied to a helpless invalid who has to be carted around in an ambulance."

"But I want to be tied to you," she told him unhappily. "I want to do everything for you . . . it would be a joy . . ."

"Well, it wouldn't be for me," he broke in.

"Oh, Mark, you can't want to stay on here for ever," Ruth pleaded. "There's a home all ready for you in Kinlocharn and I've told people I would be bringing you."

"Then you'll just have to tell them it's all off," he said flatly.

Ruth couldn't believe this was happening. She felt as if she was in the middle of a bad dream. But it was no dream, and all her protests and arguments failed to shake Mark from his decision.

How could he hurt her like this? At last pride came to her rescue and, blinking back the tears that threatened to come, she pulled off her ring and laid it on the table beside him.

"All right, Mark, if that's how you feel we'll say good-bye. I won't bother you ever again."

And without a backward look she walked from the room.

Driving north the next day, Ruth wondered drearily what had gone wrong. They had been so happy in their love, even in the anxious days which followed his accident. Could it really be because she had made all the plans without consulting him? Would all have been well if she'd asked his advice before accepting the offer of her new job?

Had it been that? If only she knew !

A GOODLY LIFE

WATER is the weathermaker! And the climate of Scotland is born in the mighty Atlantic.

With what variety! Dreich days, blithe days, roaring tempest, windless calm; snow in May and midges in November!

Yet all in all, a goodly climate. And human life, by the same Almighty Hand that makes the weather, is just as changeful.

Ambitions unfulfilled; unlikely roads leading to success. A friend's ingratitude upsets; a stranger's kindness overwhelms. Sorrow loses its edge and joy its lustre.

All in all, a goodly life!

For the God who made the seas and seasons, made also the changes and chances of life.

Bless the Almighty Hand, Whose genius lies in changefulness.

Rev. T. R. S. Campbell

At last Kinlocharn was reached. How dismal the village looked today, with a drizzle of rain falling and mist shrouding the hills. No one was visible as she drove past the cluster of houses. Her depression deepened as she turned up the short track to the school, and she wished with all her heart she hadn't agreed to come and live in this remote place.

Now she would have to go across to a neighbouring cottage and ask the woman there for the key of the house. Ruth had met Mrs Price on her previous visit and understood she'd been keeping an eye on things while the house stood empty.

Why, the door was open! Ruth stared in surprise. Surely someone hadn't broken in? That would be the last straw . . .

No, it was all right. Just inside the doorway stood the plump figure of Mrs Price, and behind her Ruth could see the welcoming glow of a real fire.

"What a day for you to arrive, Miss Taylor!" exclaimed Mrs Price. "It's too bad! But I've had the fire on since morning to warm the place up for you, and your tea is all ready.

"I know what it can be like, arriving in a new home to find it closed up and cold and empty looking, so I thought it was the least I could do to put the place into some sort of order for your coming.

"By the way, I hope you'll be happy in Kinlocharn. It's much quieter than Glasgow, of course, but it's a nice place when you get used to it, and the villagers are mostly very nice, especially to a newcomer.

"But come in now and have something to eat. You must be starving after your long journey."

RUTH followed her inside. A small table stood by the fire, laden with good things to eat. There was a plate of new scones, a cherry cake, home-made farls and biscuits, butter and honey. What kindness! She tried to stammer out thanks.

"And these flowers were sent down from Locharn House," went on Mrs Price. "We're all so pleased about you coming here, for that temporary teacher wasn't much good. It's unsettling for the bairns to have changes, so we hope you'll stay here for a long time. And how's your young man?" she asked, a sympathetic note in her voice. "Have you fixed the date for your wedding? It'll be fine when you can get him up here."

"He won't be coming," Ruth broke in abruptly. "The engagement is off. Well, thanks for what you have done, Mrs Price. I'll manage now."

Mrs Price went away, and before nightfall it was all round the village that the new school teacher wasn't bringing an invalid husband to keep her company in the comfortable little schoolhouse after all.

"Miss Taylor's changed since that day she was here before," Mrs Price told people. "She looks really unhappy. I thought her a nice cheerful girl then, but I doubt she's been hard hit by her broken engagement. We'll just have to hope it doesn't affect her work with the children.

"I daresay once she settles in and her broken heart starts to mend, she'll be all right again. These things just take a little time to get over. We'll just have to give her a bit more of a chance to fit in, that's all."

Unfortunately, as the days passed, things didn't seem to be going too well at the school. Pupils went home with complaints that lessons were dull, not at·all as they had been when Miss Sinclair was teacher. And Miss Taylor was far too severe. She wouldn't allow a whisper or smile, and dealt out boring punishments like copying bits from a dull book.

She just didn't seem to understand the Kinlocharn youngsters.

No one was more aware of the difficulties than Ruth herself. She knew her work wasn't prepared as it ought to be, and that she wasted hours every evening brooding over that last meeting with Mark. What good did it do to dwell on the matter? Resolutely she would determine to put it all out of her mind, but somehow she could never forget her last glimpse of Mark, sitting there in his wheelchair, with his face pale and set as he told her to forget all about him.

And she'd said :

" All right, I won't bother you ever again."

A S there was nothing to be done about it, Ruth must just hope this miserable time would pass. The most trying moments were when well-meaning people asked tactless questions. Yes, imagine Mrs Grant-Smith from Locharn House sailing into the schoolhouse early one morning and actually daring to ask what had gone wrong.

" We're all so worried about you, my dear," she said to Ruth in her kindly way. " It's plain you're still upset over your broken engagement. What happened? If we put our heads together we might think of some way to mend matters."

Kinlocharn folk were used to Mrs Grant-Smith's ways, but Ruth wasn't. She knew her answer wasn't very polite.

" Did you come for any special reason, Mrs Grant-Smith?" she asked coldly. " It's nearly time to start school, so if you'll excuse me . . ."

Mrs Grant-Smith never noticed when someone attempted to snub her !

" May I come, too, for a few minutes?" She beamed now. " I'll sit quiet as a mouse and watch what you do with the little people. Or would you like me to tell them a story?"

There was no doubt she was popular with the children. Ruth saw with envy how they clustered around her, chattering freely. And the story went down very well.

All the same, it was a relief to see Mrs Grant-Smith leave. Ruth couldn't get over her broken engagement being mentioned like that, and she wasn't wanting it to happen again.

It was fear of more tactless remarks that made her so reserved with other people she met. The minister's young wife came to ask if she'd like to attend a guild meeting, but she refused that, as well as an invitation along to the manse.

" I'm really very busy settling in," she said awkwardly to Heather Meredith. " You . . . you know how it is."

Heather's pretty face fell, but she didn't say any more.

Other people issued kindly invitations which Ruth also refused. The only one she accepted was when a phone call came to invite her to tea with the one person she remembered from her visit to Kinlocharn years ago. It seemed a poor return for past kindness to refuse to meet the former postmistress who had been Lisa MacLeod.

But there were new people at the post office now, and Lisa was married to the Locharn House factor, Frank Cameron.

" They live in a lovely house just a mile up the hill road," Mrs Price told Ruth. " It's only a matter of months since they married, but you'll enjoy going there, Miss Taylor, and you'll get a good tea."

The thought of a good tea had no interest for Ruth. Food seemed a bother these days, and sometimes she found herself skipping a meal, though she knew that was silly.

Well, what could she do if she lay awake half the night, then fell into a restless sleep from which she woke so late that there was time only to dress hurriedly and let the children into the school? It was like that the morning of the day when she was to go to tea with Lisa Cameron, and Ruth knew it was partly her fault that things went even worse than usual at school.

TRY as she would, she simply couldn't hold the children's attention. They yawned and fidgeted, giving stupid answers or none at all, while her weariness grew and she longed to give them all a good shaking.

Then what if Bobby Macalister didn't produce a small water-pistol and start firing it at his companions !

It didn't look like a pistol, being shaped like a man wearing Mexican costume. At first unsuspecting youngsters were quite pleased to inspect it . . . till Bobby pressed the hidden spring which released a small jet of water into their faces.

When Ruth confiscated the toy, Bobby pleaded hard for its return.

" My uncle brought me it home from Mexico, miss," he told her. " If you let me have it back I promise I'll keep it in my pocket till I go home for dinner. Oh, please, miss !"

His winning smile got the better of Ruth and she gave back the little man. A few minutes later while she wrote on the blackboard she heard a muffled scream and turned round quickly. Beth Bruce was mopping her face.

" Please, miss, Bobby shot that thing at me," Beth told the teacher indignantly.

After his promise ! Ruth was disappointed, and so annoyed that she spoke very sharply to Bobby. It was a mistake to end with some words she didn't mean in the least.

" If you can't behave, I wish you would go away home," she exclaimed impulsively.

Bobby was on his feet at once.

" All right, miss, then I'll go." He grinned. " Cheerio ! I'll tell my mum you chucked me out."

Followed by admiring and envious glances from the other children, he marched out of the door, and next minute could be seen through the window scampering down the playground.

Ruth called after him vainly. This was awful! Imagine his return home with the news that the teacher had thrown him out. Teachers were supposed to be able to control small boys of eight.

At that moment, Ruth felt that at last she had reached the end of her tether. Soon the whole village would know the poor job she was making of running the school and managing their children. And yet she seemed completely incapable of taking hold of herself and shaking off the misery which was at the heart of her difficulties. At this rate, she might well soon find herself out of a job as well, and then things would be worse than ever.

At the Macalister home ten minutes later there was certainly a good deal of astonishment when Bobby arrived. But his mother wasn't all on his side.

" If the teacher put you out you must have been

naughty," she said. " You'll go back in the afternoon, and I'll come along and have a word with Miss Taylor myself."

The interesting story was soon round the village, and again there were gloomy head-shakings about the new teacher. There were also tears from little Betty Stuart as she went home with her mother that afternoon.

" Miss Taylor's a naughty lady, Mummy," sniffed five-year-old Betty. " She threw the flowers I gave her into the wastepaper basket."

" Betty !"

" She did, Mummy, and their faces were all squashed down in the basket and their ends sticking up."

" Then that's the last time you'll get any flowers to take her," declared Mrs Stuart, thinking regretfully of the lovely chrysanthemums she had cut from the garden that morning.

TIDYING things up in the school, Ruth discovered the flowers with dismay. They must have slipped off the desk unnoticed, but, of course, she shouldn't have forgotten about them. Was that why Betty was tearful this afternoon? Oh, dear, why hadn't the child pointed out what had happened?

I'll have to leave here, thought Ruth despondently. I just make mistakes all the time. But what will I do? Where will I go?

Later on she would try to make plans. In the meantime she must remember that invitation to tea. If the house was just a mile up the road she would walk there, Ruth decided. The day was fine, and the fresh, crisp air might make her feel better.

Kinlocharn was such a picturesque place. Just now there were beautiful autumn colours all round, and when she looked back from the hill road she could see the loch far below, a deep blue under the sunshine.

This must be the factor's house, she thought presently. What a magnificent view these front windows must have ! And there at the door, looking out for her, was her hostess. Yes, she remembered Lisa Cameron, with her calm smile and her steady grey eyes.

" We miss Lisa at the post office," Mrs Price had said more than once. " She could keep her head in a crisis and she always knew what to do. Oh, she sorted out many a problem !"

But no one, not even Lisa Cameron, could put things right for Ruth Taylor. The thought was in Ruth's mind as she replied to Lisa's greeting and followed her inside to a pleasant room with just such a view as she had expected.

" How many years since we met?" Lisa said with a smile. " You did get a drenching that day."

" I certainly got a great surprise when I slipped off the jetty and found myself in very cold water," Ruth answered. " I can't think what I would have done if you hadn't been so kind to me."

They sat down. To Ruth's relief, Lisa didn't ask the usual question : " How are you liking Kinlocharn?" Instead, she spoke of the school in Perthshire where Ruth had been, then talked of events in Kinlocharn during the summer just past.

"We had more summer visitors than ever before," she went on. " Someone will have to build a hotel here before long !"

Ruth found herself relaxing. Her troubled heart warmed towards this sensible young woman who knew how to be tactful.

After a while Lisa got to her feet.

" I'll get tea now," she said. " Frank will be in any minute . . . oh, there he is now !"

THROUGH the half-open door Ruth saw a tall, fair man enter the hall. She saw the kiss he and Lisa exchanged, and felt a deep sense of loneliness. She didn't grudge the Camerons their happiness, but it only brought home once again how she had lost her own.

Frank Cameron came to talk to her while Lisa was in the kitchen. Ruth was surprised to find he knew what had happened earlier in the school. News seemed to travel fast in Kinlocharn ! But she didn't mind too much when he spoke of it.

" I hear you had trouble today with that Macalister imp," he said with a smile. " What he needs is the strap !"

" I don't approve of corporal punishment," Ruth explained. " It should be possible to discipline a small boy without it."

" It should be possible, but I'd still advise one good spanking for Master Robert," advised Frank. " You try it !"

He went on to describe some of Bobby's past mischief, and presently Lisa returned with the tea. The next hour passed very pleasantly. Indeed, Ruth felt more at ease than she had yet done since coming to Kinlocharn.

But she wasn't going to speak of her troubles to Lisa Cameron . . . no, not ever if everyone in the village advised it !

When the phone rang, Lisa went to answer it in another room. She was away quite a few minutes, and when she came back Ruth got up to go.

" Who was phoning?" Frank asked.

" Someone who thought I was still the postmistress," Lisa replied. " It seems he had phoned the post office and asked for Miss MacLeod, so the Sinclairs gave him this number. He could just as well have got the information he wanted from them," she added.

Turning to Ruth, she explained :

" When I was also in charge of the telephone exchange, anyone phoning got me first, of course. The times I've been asked things about Kinlocharn ! How big was the village, was there anywhere to stay, how was it reached . . . all these sort of things."

" You're still the best person to give information," said Frank.

The understanding smile he exchanged with his wife brought back Ruth's feeling of loneliness. She said goodbye rather hurriedly, declining the offer of a lift home, and set off down the road.

Yes, she liked the Camerons. She could quite believe Lisa was good at coping with problems, as Mrs Price said.

But I could never confide in her, thought Ruth. I could never say, Mrs Cameron, please tell me what to do about someone I love who doesn't want to see me again.

No, never in a thousand years could she say anything like that!

Nor was it necessary. In Kinlocharn it was the unexpected thing which so often happened. Ruth would have been astounded if she could have heard the conversation now taking place in the house she had just left, as Lisa told Frank more about her phone conversation with a stranger.

" He asked all the usual questions, just as I said, then he got on to the school," she stated. " When I mentioned there was a new teacher, he asked in a hesitant way how she was getting on. Frank, I'm almost certain he must be the man who was engaged to Ruth Taylor."

" But why ring you up?"

" I can't imagine, but the more I think about it the surer I am. His voice changed when he spoke of her."

" Did you say she wasn't getting on at all well?"

" Not exactly. I told him things were a bit unsettled, but we hoped everything would smooth out in time. He said, ' What do you mean —unsettled?' Then he muttered something I couldn't catch and rang off."

They looked at each other. Could the unknown caller really have been the man Ruth had hoped to marry?

" I'm sure of it," Lisa repeated slowly. " I'm so sure that I'm going to phone him back and speak to him again."

" Did you get his number then?" asked Frank.

Lisa smiled briefly.

" I haven't yet got out of the way of doing just that when it's an outside call," she returned. " I always began that way when I was at the exchange. He gave me his name, too. It's Douglas . . . Mark Douglas. I think I'll just go right now and phone him back. I must do something to help that poor girl."

GOING to the phone, she was soon connected again with Mark Douglas and explaining who she was.

" I felt I was perhaps rather hurried with you, Mr Douglas," she began. " If there's anything else you want to know, please ask me, for now I have plenty of time. When you phoned before I had a visitor in, but she's away back to the schoolhouse. It was our new teacher, Ruth Taylor."

There was a silence. Then Mark Douglas spoke.

" You . . . you said . . . you implied something was wrong. Could you tell me what it is? I . . . I knew Ruth."

" Yes, I guessed that," said Lisa in her most matter-of-fact voice. " The trouble is that she's not a bit happy here. It's affecting her work, so something will have to be done. Could you help?"

" What could I do?" exclaimed Mark Douglas. He hesitated, then seemed to take a deep breath. " Mrs Cameron, I may as well tell you, Ruth and I were engaged. It seemed unfair to keep her tied to me for ever, so I broke it off. I kept wondering how she was getting on, and at last I remembered her saying once how you were kind to her. I thought if I phoned and asked a few questions I might hear . . . but I didn't expect to be told she was really unhappy. So that's two of us," he added in a low tone.

Then if he was unhappy, too, why on earth didn't he get in touch with Ruth again, thought Lisa rather impatiently. He could have phoned direct to her in the first place. Oh, dear, now he was saying gloomily there was nothing to be done about it. What would she answer to that? A sudden inspiration came to her.

"Mr Douglas, why not come up to Kinlocharn and see Ruth?" she asked. "I could easily arrange accommodation for you in the village. It's always more satisfactory to see people, isn't it, when there's any awkwardness.?"

"Come to Kinlocharn?" echoed Mark Douglas. If she'd suggested flying to the moon he couldn't have sounded more taken aback. Then suddenly a new resolute note came into his voice.

"It's an idea!" he said.

Why, it was as if he liked it being assumed he was as able to travel as anyone.

"Please don't tell Ruth anything about this," he begged Lisa. "I think I could get someone to take me as far as Glasgow, then surely I could manage a train journey . . . in the guard's van with my chair if needs be! Mrs Cameron, how far would the train take me?"

"To Inverness," Lisa informed him. "After that it might be more difficult so my husband and I will meet you at the station and bring you to Kinlocharn. I can arrange for you to get rooms from a Mrs Price, who lives in a cottage near the school. She's a retired nurse and will look after you well."

Even as she made the arrangements, Lisa knew a few tremors. Would a disabled man really manage a long train journey all by himself? Would Ruth really be glad to see him?

"I wish now I'd never suggested he came up," Lisa lamented to her husband later on. "Why do I always get involved in other people's difficulties?"

Frank was smiling as he took her reassuringly into his arms.

"Dearest Lisa, what is it the Kinlocharn folk say? 'Lisa always knows what is best to do.' It'll be the same this time, you'll see."

B Y the following Wednesday everyone in the village except Ruth knew that her former fiancé was coming to stay with Mrs Price.

"It was he who broke off the engagement, so what a grand surprise she'll get." The kindly women smiled to each other.

The first surprise Ruth got was when she answered her phone about seven o'clock to hear Mrs Price on the line.

"Could you come over, please, Miss Taylor?" asked Mrs Price. "As soon as you can."

Before Ruth could ask why, she had rung off. A little uneasily, Ruth slipped on a coat and set out. Could something be wrong? No, there was a broad beam on Mrs Price's face when she opened the door of her neat little cottage.

" Just go in there, Miss Taylor," she said, indicating the room she let out to visitors every summer.

All unsuspecting, Ruth entered. Then she stopped short, staring. Was this a dream? It couldn't be true ! It couldn't really be Mark, sitting there in his chair by a glowing peat fire !

" Mark !" she gasped unbelievingly.

" Ruth !" he exclaimed. " Is something wrong?"

For all at once she was white as a sheet. The long time of worry, the inadequate food and the sleepless nights were taking their toll. Before his dismayed eyes she slid to the ground in a faint.

MARK tried to pull himself to his feet. He clung to the mantelpiece as he shouted for Mrs Price. She came running, understanding quickly what had occurred.

" Just you sit down, Mr Douglas," she advised. " It's only a faint."

Indeed, Ruth was coming round fast. In another minute she was on her feet, going shakily to kneel beside Mark while they exchanged a long kiss. Mrs Price withdrew tactfully.

Nothing like a good shock on both sides to put matters right, she decided !

" I had to come to see how you were getting on," Mark told Ruth. " I think it's you who needs looking after, not me."

" But how did you get here?" Ruth asked him. " Did someone bring you?"

" I came to Inverness by myself," Mark informed her with satisfaction. " Mr and Mrs Cameron met me at the station and brought me here in their car."

" The Camerons?" exclaimed Ruth. " They met you?"

She couldn't understand in the least.

Mark soon explained. He told how he'd longed for news of her, and how he had remembered the name of the postmistress at Kinlocharn . . . no longer Miss MacLeod, as he'd discovered.

" When Mrs Cameron asked why I didn't come here, I could hardly believe it," he went on. " People have all been so busy protecting and cushioning me in their well-meaning way. It did me good to be left to decide for myself if I could manage the journey. It did me more good than anything ! So now I'll just stay on here for a little, then we'll be married and I'll move in with you. All right, darling?"

" Very much all right," she whispered.

How wrong she had been to try to assume all responsibility, to make all the plans and leave Mark feeling useless and helpless ! She'd never do that again, Ruth resolved.

And now she could answer the question she had so often dreaded.

" Tell me, love, how do you really like Kinlocharn?"

" I think it's the nicest place in the world !" she replied with a radiant smile.

Not Such A Cushy Job !

S ANDRA ANDREWS looked at the lovely countryside around her
which seemed to shimmer through a mist of tears. When she and
Barry Lyall had become engaged, only two weeks ago, she had
looked forward to bringing him home, and walking with him along the
river path which she loved so much. But now, instead of sharing that
joy, it was being spoilt by their first quarrel !

And all because of a beautiful, delicate gold brooch of fern and hill
heather picked out in freshwater pearls.

It was only two days ago that Sandra had brought Barry home to
Thornhead to meet her parents. She was in her last year at university,
taking an English degree, and Barry was also there, doing his finals

by ALICE MACKIE

in Architecture. Barry's father had his own office in Edinburgh, and he would be going there as soon as he had finished his training.

"We could live at home, darling," he said eagerly. "There's only Father and Aunt Nora there since Mother died, and I think you and she would get on well. Then as soon as I'm on my feet, we could look for a house to do us till we can build our own !"

"It sounds wonderful, Barry." Sandra's eyes were shining. She had met Nora Lyall and had liked the quiet, elderly woman, feeling grateful that she and Mr Lyall were willing to have her in their home.

"There's plenty of room," Sandra told her mother, happily. "It's a really big house, and Miss Lyall isn't a critical type. Besides, I'd like to get a job for a year or two and make use of my degree."

"Well, so long as you're happy," Mrs Andrews had said.

She looked round her own poky kitchen. This had been their first home when she and Sam married and in those days he had wonderful visions of a happy future for them both.

"It isn't much, Janet," he had said, "but wait till you see. I'll get on. I'm starting with one travelling shop, but I'll soon have more than one then, perhaps, a fine business in Edinburgh. I'll be able to give you every home comfort in a year or two . . . holidays abroad . . ."

"Oh, Sam !" Janet had laughed. "That sounds wonderful, but at the moment I'll settle for having the kitchen painted."

The years had crept past and the cottage had just grown a little more shabby. Their greatest pride had been when Sam changed his old van for a new one, though his profit margin had remained small.

At first Janet had sighed, wondering how many people had found themselves with a little extra something from her husband, but she knew he would never change, and loved him as he was.

Nor had there been any more talk of a fleet of vans and a fine business in Edinburgh, and Sam seemed to have forgotten about it until Sandra announced she was bringing her new fiancé home for the first time.

I DOUBT the young man won't find much architectural beauty in here," Sam remarked, his eyes sweeping round the kitchen. It never seemed to get that coat of paint !

"None of that," Janet warned him. "It's our home, and Sandra isn't the girl to be ashamed of us."

"No, but . . . but maybe I'm a bit disappointed in myself," Sam said and, before Janet could stop him, he had quietly taken his cap from behind the door and made for the river walk, a place to which they had all taken their troubled thoughts from time to time.

When Barry's car had rolled up the following day, however, both Janet and Sam were there to greet their daughter and the man she loved. Barry Lyall was a tall young man with a thin, clever face and long, slender hands. He looked as though he had never done a day's work in his life, thought Sam, as he shook hands.

Sandra looked radiant. The following day was her twenty-first birthday, and Janet had arranged a small party, just for the four of them. She thought of the jeweller's box which was tucked away in the sideboard drawer, all done up with fancy wrapping paper. She and Sam had saved hard for the gift and now they could hardly wait to present it to Sandra.

"We're going to choose a ring next week," Sandra had told her, happily.

"Is it to be your twenty-first present from Barry?" her mother had asked.

"Mainly . . . though he says he'll have another small gift, too. I didn't care if we didn't have a ring, and just bought one for the wedding, but he's a bit old-fashioned that way. He likes things to be done properly.'

"Quite right, too," Janet agreed, though her eyes sobered a little. Everything about Barry proclaimed the kind of prosperity they, themselves, would never have. She looked at Sandra, biting her lip.

"I . . . I hope Barry's folks don't mind about us, well, not having much. We're maybe not their kind of people."

"Oh, Mum!" Sandra's voice drifted into silence as the door clicked quietly. They hadn't noticed Sam coming in, and now he had slipped back out again.

"Your father is a wee bit sensitive about not making a better go of things," Janet explained. "Sometimes he feels he hasn't done his best."

"I've never heard of anything so daft," Sandra argued. "Who cares about that nowadays?"

T HE words sounded slightly different now, however, when Barry used them to Sandra. The previous evening she had glowed with excitement after changing into a pretty new dress, bought specially for her twenty-first birthday party.

"Can't I help?" she asked her mother.

"You can't even touch a spoon," she was told. "Go into the sitting-room and talk to Barry and your father."

Barry had appeared a moment later, wearing a dark suit and coloured

UNLESS

UNLESS you seek the wealth there is in living,
And learn to find the best in every day;
UNLESS you know the pleasure gained in giving,
— You'll never feel the sunshine's brightest ray.

UNLESS you try to ease a heart of sorrow,
And spare the time to share another's load;
UNLESS you look towards that bright tomorrow,
And scatter seeds of Friendship on the road.

UNLESS you keep the lamp of faith well burning,
And make your hope sincere, and strong, and true;
UNLESS you take an honest joy in learning
The daily lessons life presents to you.

UNLESS you count these things your greatest treasure,
And be yourself the best that you can be;
— You'll never taste of life in richest measure,
And you'll never reap the Final Victory.

PEGGY BLAND

shirt with tie to match. He was carrying a small, gift-wrapped parcel.

" I'll take her away, Mrs Andrews." He grinned. " Don't you know when you aren't wanted ?" he teased Sandra.

As he pushed her out of the dining-room door, he turned to Mrs Andrews and handed her the small parcel.

" Put it beside Sandra's plate," he whispered.

" All right, Barry."

There had been other gifts from relatives and friends with dozens of cards, but Sandra felt most excited by the two gifts beside her plate when they all sat down to dinner. She hesitated, then glanced at her mother.

" I'll open this one first," she said, selecting theirs, and saw the eagerness and pride on their faces as she carefully unwrapped the jeweller's box and threw back the lid. It was the prettiest of brooches which nestled in the box ; a lovely rose, fashioned in silver, with a small garnet at the heart to give it warmth and life.

" Oh, Mum, Dad, it's beautiful." Sandra jumped up to kiss them.

" I'm glad you like it," Janet Andrews told her tremulously, while Sam cleared his throat.

Sandra picked up the other parcel, smiling at Barry. At first they had planned to buy her ring for this party, but she had wanted her parents to meet Barry and get to know him before she wore a ring.

Now she drew out a small white leather box and opened the lid. For a moment there was stunned silence as she lifted out the beautiful dainty brooch with the tracery of fern and bracken in gold and freshwater pearls in all their lovely colours of cream, pink and mauve.

Her mother was the first to speak.

" It's exquisite," she breathed.

" Beautiful." Sam nodded while Barry grinned happily.

" You're well off for brooches now, love," her father continued.

" Yes."

WHY did Barry have to go and buy something so expensive, she thought with annoyance. She realised that he couldn't possibly know her parents were buying the rose, and she looked at both of them as her mother began serving dinner. They were both smiling happily, but remembering her conversation with her mother, she wondered if they weren't feeling that the gold brooch, which Barry had so casually presented, didn't detract from the silver one she knew they must have saved hard to buy.

" I'm glad you like it," Barry was saying. " As a matter of fact . . ."

" I can start by wearing my rose one," Sandra said rather loudly, pinning it in and shutting the box on the gold bracken one. The smile dimmed on Barry's face as she put the two boxes behind her on the sideboard.

" It was too much," Sandra told him the next day as they walked round the river path. " Couldn't you see that ? When we were planning to buy a ring."

" No, I don't see it," Barry said. " The two things are quite different. The ring will be our engagement ring and this was for your twenty-first.

I'd planned to tell you more about it, but I doubt if you'll be interested now."

"But Mum and Dad saved so hard for the rose brooch."

"Then you must value it because of that. Only don't belittle mine because I didn't. If you ask me, it's as bad to look down on my gift just because it was expensive as the other way round. People just don't think that way nowadays. It's old-fashioned."

Sandra wanted to throw herself into his arms, saying she was sorry and she should have pinned in both gifts and made no difference between them, but the look on his face stopped her.

"And I hope you can explain to your father that there is more than one way to do a good hard day's work," Barry went on. "I've tried, but I don't think that he believes me."

"There are degrees of hard work." Sandra thought of the mornings she had seen her father go out early into the bleakest of weathers, to return tired and weary by evening.

"Yes, but there again we can all just do our best according to what we are," Barry insisted.

THEY walked home in silence, while Sandra surreptitiously brushed away a few tears. Somehow it had all seemed so simple in Edinburgh, but out here at Thornhead things were intruding in a way she would never have believed possible. She and Barry had always seen eye to eye about everything, but now she wondered if their values were really the same, and if they really would understand one another. And would there be even greater differences because of this if she went to share their home with the Lyalls ?

"I shall have to leave soon," Barry told her. "I've got work to do on a project."

"That's all right, I'll tell Mother," she said evenly.

As they returned to the house, however, they knew something was wrong when Mrs Andrews came hurrying out to meet them.

"Oh, thank goodness you're back," she said to Sandra. "It's your father. He slipped getting out of the van near old Mrs Wallace's cottage, and they think his leg is broken. I'm going to the hospital now."

"We'll come, too," Barry told her. "We can go in my car."

Mrs Andrews looked at him gratefully.

"Thank you, Barry. I'll be so glad of your help."

"Don't worry about the van," Barry said as they sat beside Sam Andrews' bed in hospital. The older man looked white and shaken, but hoped to get home to rest in a few days' time. "I'll take it out."

"You'll never manage it," the older man told him weakly. "There's more to it than just driving up to a house, or through a village. There's the price of things . . ."

"You'll have a price list." Barry brushed aside the objection.

"Ay. And the route . . . Maybe Sandra had better go with you."

"There isn't room for both of us. No, I'll manage. Surely it's not all that difficult !"

There was an impatient note in the young man's voice, and a glint of humour came into Sam's eyes, followed by a strangely thoughtful look. There were other aspects he hadn't mentioned, and he wondered what the lad would make of those!

"If you think you can do it, I'll be very grateful," he said.

"Don't worry, Mr Andrews, I'll take care of it," Barry told him confidently.

BARRY set off bright and early the next morning, having done his best to see that the van was stocked according to Sandra's advice, as she had taken on the paper work. The routes for the day had been marked out on a map and some sort of estimate made of how long it should take him.

By lunch-time, Barry was well behind, and beginning to have new respect for Sam Andrews. As Sandra had said, there were degrees of hard work!

At the first village he had found his customers eager to be helpful and full of sympathy for Sam, though one or two were determined to get what was due to them.

"None of your bacon in a packet," one elderly woman told him firmly. "Cut me a nice piece of lean ham, nice and thin."

Barry made several attempts at the slicing machine before his customer reluctantly accepted his efforts, saying she could have done with it thinner.

"And don't forget old Mrs Brown," she went on.

"Who is she?"

"Over there at the end cottage. She leaves a basket out for Sam when she's away, and she got on the bus to go and get her pension."

It was some time before he located the basket just behind the door of the shed and managed to decipher the spidery handwriting on the message.

By the time he got home in the evening Barry was very tired, and Sandra almost as much so. She had been kept busy at home doing the accounts.

"Well, did you find it hard work?" she asked smiling.

As soon as she had added up some figures, she was going to lay it all aside and thank Barry properly for what he was doing. But he misinterpreted the smile.

"I can cope," he said briefly. "It only takes a bit of commonsense."

As the days passed, Barry's respect for Sam Andrews grew by leaps and bounds, and he began to appreciate that the rewards were small for the work involved, and to know how Sally had felt when she saw the lovely rose brooch.

In an odd sort of way he was enjoying the challenge, and said as much when the older man got home from hospital a few days later.

"I must say I would never have realised there was so much variety to a job," he said.

"Ay, it isn't as easy as folks imagine," Sandra's father grinned.

"It isn't only the van and selling from it, it's the customers. Besides drinking tea and eating cakes, I've carried letters to be delivered or posted, wool to be matched from one village to another and I've mended more broken items than I've done in the past year. It always seemed easier than just taking the message to someone else !"

Sam's eyes were beginning to twinkle.

" They've been taking advantage of you, lad. I'm sorry, I should have warned you."

" You mean you don't have to do anything like that ?"

Sam coloured self-consciously, then grinned again.

" I know who needs a firm hand ! Did old Mrs Brown want you to look at her stove ?"

" Oh, that was a blockage in one of the flues," Barry told him. " I've written down instructions for her to have it mended. It's a big job."

" You mean you knew how it could be fixed ?" the older man asked.

This time it was Barry's turn to colour at the surprise and respect in Sam Andrews' voice.

" Well, I learned about things like that in my training."

" That's a fine young man," Sam told his wife and daughter later. " He certainly knows how to do a good day's work !"

O N the night before Barry was due to return to Edinburgh, Sandra opened the white leather box again and looked at the beautiful brooch. Over the past few days her love and admiration for Barry had grown steadily, and she felt deeply ashamed of the ungracious way she had accepted his gift. She had wanted so much to apologise, but somehow she felt that a barrier had grown up between them.

Her parents had worried about the differences between them, but they didn't know the truth. She had allowed the pettiness of wrong values to creep into their relationship. Barry had been right about the brooches. She ought to have valued them equally out of love, not setting one aside because she thought it was too valuable and had been bought too easily.

Yet over the week she had come to see that Barry had learned to put value on her father's work and in return her father had gained a great deal of respect for Barry's.

She still had the box in her hand when Barry walked into the kitchen, his eyes growing a little bleak at the sight of it.

" I . . . I was just looking at the brooch," she began.

" Oh."

" Barry, I'm so sorry," she whispered.

A moment later she was in his arms.

" Sandra darling, don't let's quarrel over a brooch. If you don't like it, then we can get another. I was going to tell you before, but I couldn't seem to find a right moment, but that brooch was Mother's, and Father asked me to give it to you. He loved her, you see, as I love you and only the best was good enough for her, just as I'd like it to be that way for you, too. I shall always want to give you my best, just as your parents have given you theirs."

" I know." Sandra nodded, trying not to let tears thicken her voice. " I hope I'll be able to give you my best, too."

And as he kissed her, Barry was sure she would.

A SUNSHINE-SPREADING WEDDING

BY JEAN MELVILLE

THE wedding between Elizabeth Shaw and Martin Napier excited practically the whole village of Nether Leighton. For one thing, Martin Napier was the young minister of a neighbouring parish, though the villagers had known and loved him since a boy. His father was their own beloved Reverend Robert Napier, and he would be performing the ceremony.

In fact, the village had been waiting eight years to see this wedding take place. A month or two after Elizabeth and Martin had become engaged, Mrs Shaw had died, leaving a young family of four to bring up, besides Elizabeth, who was then only twenty. Talk of the forthcoming wedding had soon died down as Elizabeth took on the care of her father, three younger brothers, and her sister Molly.

The three boys were now doing well in their chosen careers, and Molly was in her first year at training college. It was she who had urged Elizabeth not to keep Martin waiting any longer when she knew they had been discussing getting married at last.

" There's still Father and Walter," Elizabeth said worriedly.

" Father and Walter are doing well in business together," Molly pointed out. " Walter is a pretty good glazier, according to Father, and we can soon get a housekeeper to keep an eye on them both. Jim and Eric are married, and I "—Molly's cheeks coloured faintly—" I'll be at home all through the holidays."

" What about that young man you keep mentioning? John Goudie, isn't it?"

" We're just friends," Molly said shortly.

" Well, maybe a quiet wedding. I'll see Martin."

" A quiet wedding !" Molly cried. " The whole of Nether Leighton will be wanting to be in on it. You've got a hope, Liz."

Mrs Ethel Grant heard the news in the bus coming hom from Castleford, though it only caused her mild interest, she was so deep in her own thoughts. She had spent a tiring day in town looking for threads, buttons and zipp fasteners for the work she had in hand, and she sighed deeply, thinking of the recent differences of opinion she'd been having with her husband, Jack. It had all blown up the previous evening when Jack had come home late after a very busy day at the local bakery and found her still at her sewing machine.

Jack thrust away his own fatigue as he looked at his wife. They had been married ten years, and until just over a year ago Ethel had been happy to use her skill as a dressmaker in providing her own clothes. However, at a time when he had been forced to stay off work she had taken in a few odd jobs to help out their income. Gradually, the work

had snowballed, and now part of their living-room was piled high with garments.

"Sit still," he commanded. "I'll put the kettle on and we can get supper between us. Luckily I've brought some pies home.

"And put your sewing away," he continued firmly. "I want to talk to you, dear."

"All right, Jack," she agreed. "I'm afraid it will all have to keep."

"You've got to give it up," he said quietly.

"Give what up?"

"All this." He waved a hand towards her pile of sewing and mending.

"I can't, Jack. I'm sorry, my dear, but I'm afraid it's essential now for me to earn money."

It was his turn to flush.

"I can work overtime . . ."

"No!" she said firmly. "You wore yourself out before. No, I'll just have to keep on working, at least until things are better.

Jack said nothing for a long while.

"I don't mind doing it, I like sewing," she assured him.

" Though I do get fed up altering clothes and mending zipps, I must admit."

" Then why do it?" he asked. " You're a trained dressmaker, so can't you make new garments for people instead? Wouldn't you like that better?"

" I'd love it," she confessed honestly. " But I can't refuse people when they come with alterations. Nobody ever asks me to do anything new."

" They would if they knew that you only made new clothes. What's that there, for instance?"

" It's a coat for Mrs Barclay. The lining got torn."

" Couldn't she sew it herself?"

Ethel pursed her lips.

" Well . . . I don't know."

Jack was finding out what other jobs were there, and assessing the small charges she was making.

" If you ask me, you're only encouraging young people not to do their own work," he said at length.

" That's not true!" she flashed. " Most of them have young children . . ."

" And if we had children, don't you think you would be happy to do your mending by the fireside of an evening, after they were in bed?"

Ethel nodded, her eyes rather wistful.

" Come on, love," he said, putting his arm round her. " Think about it. I know you like dressmaking, but I don't like to see you snowed under with this sort of work. Just think about it, that's all."

IN the morning Ethel had gone to town for new threads and other items, and she had thought of nothing else all day. Could Jack be right?

As she walked back home and approached her own gate her heart sank when she saw that another prospective customer was ringing the door bell, the usual bundle under her arm.

However, as she walked up the path and the figure turned to greet her she saw that it was Miss Shaw who was going to marry young Mr Napier, the minister.

" Hello, Mrs Grant," Elizabeth said. " I was just feeling disappointed that you were out."

" Please come in," Ethel said quietly. " I've just been into the town."

" I hope it's a convenient time."

" Of course it is. Would you like to share a pot of tea with me, then you can tell me how I can help you?"

If you drive along the road from Kintail to Kyle of Lochalsh, on the way to Skye, you're sure to be impressed by the picturesque island castle of Eilean Donan. Built in the Middle Ages, it has been the scene of many exciting events and was damaged in the Jacobite struggles, but recently has been extensively restored, and is now regularly open to the public.

Eilean Donan Castle   *J. Campbell Kerr*

"I'm getting married," Elizabeth began after they were settled.

"Yes, I had heard. I'm very happy for you."

"My fiancé wants a big wedding," Elizabeth went on shyly. "Mr Napier will marry us, of course."

"That will make it an exciting wedding."

"Yes, and I was wondering if you could make my wedding dress?"

Elizabeth got up and opened the parcel she had brought, and Ethel Grant gasped when she saw the yards of beautiful, white, watered silk which tumbled out.

"Oh, it's beautiful," she breathed.

"My mother bought it just before she died," Elizabeth told her softly. "I'd just got engaged, and she wanted me to have a lovely dress, a sort of picture dress . . ."

Ethel's face was still shining with the excitement of it when Jack came home, and new energy flowed as she set out supper for them both.

"You were right," she told him. "I'm only going to take alterations from people who can't do them for themselves. But when they all see Miss Shaw's wedding dress, things are going to be different. Oh, Jack, how I'm looking forward to that wedding!"

YOU were right, darling, you and Molly," Elizabeth told Martin when he called to see her the following evening. "The wedding is going to be shared by the village. You should have seen Mrs Grant's face when I asked her to make my wedding gown. I'm sure no one would make a better job of it.

I've ordered the wedding cake, and Mrs Grant's delight in making my dress makes me wonder if anyone in the village would like to do the flowers."

"Such as?"

"Miss Graham?"

"Miss Graham! You must be joking," Martin said. "We've all tried, but Father has given up asking her to take part in anything. Since she retired as schoolmistress she's been getting more and more stand-offish."

"I know." Elizabeth's eyes were serious. "But I don't believe she really means it. That's why I wondered if you'd like to ask her."

Claire Graham often wondered why she had stayed on in Nether Leighton after she retired, though at the time it had seemed much the best thing to do. For years she had lived in the schoolhouse, but it was a tied house and shortly before she had to leave it her present cottage came up for sale. It was a small house, with a long garden which suited her admirably, and the price had been right. Miss Graham had bought it joyfully, and after the village gave her a retirement gift of a television set at a social occasion specially arranged, she had felt that her cup of happiness was full.

At first she hadn't noticed that things had begun to be different for her. She had never had much time to watch television before.

But now she found that time was hanging a little heavily on her hands when it got too dark to work in the garden, and she had been happy to relax and turn on the television.

Nor had the deafness which troubled her a little been too much of a nuisance. A little turn at the knob had ensured that it was loud enough for her to hear, and she had no near neighbours to complain about the noise.

Miss Graham began to notice after a few weeks, however, that she was having fewer visitors than she had hoped. She still saw local people when she went shopping, but now a subtle difference had entered their relationship. They seemed shy of her, and gradually she could feel a wall of reserve growing up between her and the rest of the community.

MISS GRAHAM had worried about this, and when Mr Napier, the minister, called one evening she had tentatively broached the subject.

" I—I just wondered if there was any way I could help," she said finally. " I feel a bit lost."

" That's only natural," Mr Napier told her gently. " And my wife would likely be glad of your help. She always seems to have too much to do. Now, let me see . . . the choir?"

" Oh, bless me, I can't sing!" Miss Graham exclaimed. " I couldn't manage more than a squeak."

" Well, maybe the Ladies Fellowship. It's on the first and third Wednesdays of every month."

" I could try that," Miss Graham agreed.

But it wasn't a success. The president of the Fellowship had been looking for new ideas for Christmas at the first meeting, and Miss Graham had been full of them. She stood up, feeling very much at home lecturing from the body of the hall, but her words had met with faint applause and her ideas were obviously not appreciated.

So she had begun to accept her own loneliness and isolation, and even to covet it, while she made a picture out of her garden and a lonely haven out of her cottage, with the television for company.

Martin Napier had to ring several times before Miss Graham eventually came to the door. She looked taken aback for a moment when she saw him, then she smiled. Martin had been a former pupil and a favourite one.

" I hope I'm not disturbing you," he greeted her. " I can only spare a few moments myself, as I have a church meeting this evening in my own parish."

" Do come in," she invited, and as he looked meaningfully at the television she went and turned it off. " You'll have some tea?"

" Please," he said.

" Now, how can I help you," she said, adding rather dryly, " I assume it isn't just a social call."

Martin flushed.

" Social and business. I expect you know Elizabeth and I are getting married soon. Well, we wondered if you would like to do the flowers."

" Why are you asking me?" she said at length. " No one has wanted me for anything special for quite some time."

Martin drew a deep breath.

" You can't blame the village entirely for that, Miss Graham," he said quietly. " Maybe they've been at fault over some things, but you've been making it clear that you enjoy your own company best.

He looked at her squarely.

" I mean, you wouldn't even open your door at first. It took you all your time to open it to me this evening."

" But you only rang once !"

" No, I rang many times, but I knew you must be in and I'd promised Elizabeth that I would see you this evening if I could."

Miss Graham was looking puzzled.

" It must have been the television," she said slowly. " I'm a little deaf, you see. I do the same with my radio during the day. Oh . . . do you think . . . ? "

She and Martin looked at each other.

" I do," he said. " I think there's been misunderstandings all round. Everyone must have felt you wanted to keep your own company and you—you've been thinking no one called. Perhaps no one has for some time."

" Then I'll have to go to them," Miss Graham said thoughtfully. " Only this time I'll see that they understand that they haven't got the teacher !"

" Can you start by doing the flowers?" asked Martin, smiling again.

" I'll be delighted," she answered.

MOLLY tried on the bridesmaid's dress which Mrs Grant had made, and sighed with satisfaction. It was high-waisted, and the turquoise silk made her young face glow. What would John think when he saw her wearing this dress? If he saw her wearing it . . .

" Shall I send John Goudie an invitation?" Elizabeth had asked. " You'll want him to be there, won't you?"

Molly flushed and bit her lip, then her chin lifted.

" Yes, please, Elizabeth. It's just that . . . he has no family, you see, and he's always lived in a town. He . . . he might find the village rather strange."

Elizabeth's eyes had opened wide.

" In what way?"

" Oh, just different, that's all," said Molly. " He'll enjoy it."

She had said the last words half defiantly, but the truth was she didn't really know whether John Goudie would enjoy the wedding or not.

John had been rather quiet after he received Elizabeth's invitation to the wedding.

" You will come, won't you, John?" Molly asked. " I mean, I'd have been asking you down to Nether Leighton anyway to meet my family."

" Oh, of course I'll come," he assured her, but there hadn't been much eagerness in his voice. " Won't I have to book in at a hotel somewhere?"

" Not if you don't mind a single bed in our smallest bedroom. It isn't bad. You could have had Jim's room or Eric's, but they're coming home for the wedding and they're both married."

John had looked quieter than ever.

" The single room will be fine," he said.

" I'll meet you at the station," Molly said. " I'll have to be at home for a few days helping Elizabeth."

" That's fine," John agreed. " I'll be there."

BUT now as she walked up to the station, Molly's eyes were worried. She couldn't deny to herself that John was important in her life, but so were her family. It wouldn't be a happy situation if they didn't get along with each other. She expected differences, of course, but there were some basic things which had to be the same.

John looked very young as he leapt off the train. He had had his hair cut, and he wore a much more sober suit than his usual corduroys and zipped-up jacket.

" Hello, Molly," he greeted her.

" Hello, John. I hope you don't mind walking. It isn't far, and you can see the village."

For the first time since they had met, they felt uncomfortable with each other, and though Molly chattered brightly, telling him all about the village and its inhabitants, John seemed more awkward and shy than ever.

" And here is the church," Molly said. " Would you like to see inside, John? You can leave your case in the porch. Nobody will take it."

He smiled more naturally.

" I doubt if there's anything worth taking, except for a travel clock, your sister's wedding present."

He put down the case and together they went quietly into the empty church. But it wasn't quite empty. Standing near the altar was a tall, thin figure, carefully arranging a bowl of flowers, and even as Molly was going to go forward and introduce John, she saw Miss Graham stand back and look round her furtively.

John had hung back, his hand on her arm, and now she was glad he did so as Miss Graham suddenly burst into song.

The Lord's my Shepherd, I'll not want, she sang, her voice thin and reedy, then becoming completely tuneless as she gave it more power.

Molly's eyes flew in horror to John's face. She expected him to laugh, but instead the grip on her arm tightened and he indicated that they tiptoed out again.

" Who is she?" he asked.

" Miss Graham. She used to be our schoolmistress."

" She's just trying herself out," John said. " I used to want to do that, but the church always seemed to be busy when I was there and I could never have a go on my own."

Molly drew a deep breath. He hadn't laughed at Miss Graham. He had understood. Thankfully, she knew that the basic things were there.

" This way, John," she said, taking his arm, " and I'm so glad you've come. I'm proud of my family, but I'm so very proud of you, too."

It was going to be a wonderful wedding, Molly thought, a sunshine-spreading wedding !

Funny What Love Can Do

by

Peggy Maitland

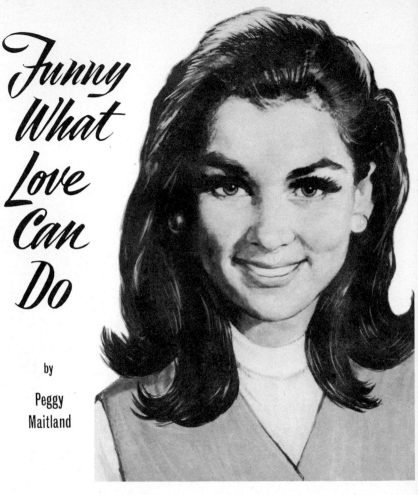

JENNIFER HAMPTON lay hunched up on her side watching the snow falling outside her bedroom window. She closed her eyes, and, in the few minutes that she slept, the room darkened and the window became a mirror, so that she wakened with the impression that the snowstorm was a dazzling, dramatic performance.

Each snowflake fell faster than the one before, hurling itself against the window-pane with frenzied intensity, then dancing dejectedly back from the promised warmth, fluttering and forlorn.

Through Jennifer's half-closed eyelids the window became a cinema screen. She could almost hear the thrilling beat of the music and feel the terror building up inside her until she just couldn't bear to look any longer.

She lay still and tense in the darkness, remembering last night,

118

reliving the agonising moment when the music rose to an unbearable crescendo and the whole cinema audience had held its breath waiting for the unknown, unimaginable monster to flash on the screen.

In that very last second Jennifer had closed her eyes and turned her head away, twisting round in her seat. Out of the darkness Michael's arms had caught and held her, his lips meeting hers in a fleeting kiss, tender and yet passionate. In the shelter of his loving arms she felt protected and cherished, as if she would never again have reason to fear anything or anybody. Her fluttering heartbeats forgot the terror of the film and became the glittering wings of a new and wonderful emotion.

" I'm in love." Her heart sang the melody of the words that floated in her mind like all the brilliant colours of the universe.

L ET'S go," he had whispered, and she had risen to her feet obediently, still so much under the spell of that surprising kiss that she had been oblivious to the weird sounds and scenes on the wide screen as they edged their way along the row and made their way to the exit of the darkened cinema.

" All right now?" Michael had asked once they were on the pavement outside. " We could have gone to that other film. I didn't know you'd be afraid."

They were walking slowly, and she glanced at him shyly, uncertainly.

" I'm an awful coward," she said quietly, pushing her hands into her jacket pockets, suddenly afraid that the brushing of his lips against hers had meant nothing at all.

" I don't think you're a coward." There was a world of tenderness in Michael's voice. " I think you were pretty brave, trying to pretend that you weren't bothering when all the time I could sense that you were terrified."

" Could you? Did you know?" Jennifer stopped and turned to look at him at last, brushing a wisp of hair back from her forehead.

" Yes, of course I knew." He smiled into her eyes, and caught hold of her hand before she could put it in her pocket again.

" I suppose it's silly of me," she said as they began to walk along, hand in hand. " But those films always seem too real."

He nodded sympathetically, and as she looked again into his brown eyes she knew that he understood how awful it was to be timid and easily frightened. There was no need to tell him of the laughter and teasing which had always pursued her like a mocking echo. Often she had comforted herself with the thought that they didn't mean to be unkind ; that her parents, for instance, laughed from a genuine desire to diminish her fears. She had learned to accept the teasing of her brother and sisters and friends, and in doing so she had managed to overcome some of the terrors of everyday life.

Sometimes, she admitted to herself, her method of conquering her fears was still the childish one of closing her eyes, holding her breath and plunging headlong into whatever it was she must do.

Since she was the youngest of the family she had always had to go upstairs to bed first every night, and she had found that closing her

The People's Friend Annual

eyes and running was the only way that she could bring herself to pass the shadows that lurked on the stairway.

And now, although she was seventeen years old, the step that creaked, third from the top, still had the power to make her leap into the safety of her bedroom and fumble with shaking fingers for the light switch.

Nobody knew about that, though, nor of the way she dashed along the part of the avenue where the branches of the trees hung over the wall of the Wallaces' house with whispering, rustling menace.

" What a fanciful child you are," her mother used to say with an amused smile. " Your terrors are all in your imagination."

AND in a way her mother had been right, she had grown out of being afraid of lots of things, and as for the others, well, she could always close her eyes.

" I tried to keep my eyes closed," she confided to Michael, able to smile now that she knew he understood. " But I just couldn't help looking."

" I know." He squeezed her hand gently. " A sort of compulsion. Worse than when you are wondering whether or not there's anything there. You have to look, just in case you miss something."

" Yes." She nodded. " When there's a horror film on television at home I have to go out of the room before it starts, otherwise I just can't keep from peeping, even if I've got a good book to read and sit with my back to the set !" She stopped abruptly with an embarrassed laugh, aware that she ought to have refused his invitation.

" We'll avoid horror films in future then." Michael smiled as he spoke, and there was a teasing note in his voice, but she knew that underneath was reassurance.

" When you asked me to go out with you, I didn't want to refuse."

" Just as well you didn't," he answered solemnly, " otherwise I'd never have plucked up the courage to ask you again."

His lop-sided grin was boyish and disarming, and Jennifer felt her heart turning with an overwhelming affection. Their eyes met with a look of exquisite tenderness, and, almost unconsciously, they moved closer together. As they walked through the darkened streets, their steps matched so perfectly that it was as if they were one person.

Remembering, Jennifer could almost have believed that they had walked on a cloud, surrounded by a cocoon of clouds in a magical silence where no words were needed to tell of the awe-inspiring love that they had found. She lay with her eyes closed, remembering . . .

" What on earth are you doing up here in the dark?" The door seemed to burst open in the same instant as the light flashed on, and Mrs Hampton's brisk question shattered the silence and the imagining.

Jennifer half sat up, rubbing her eyes, dazzled by the light and bemused by the unexpected sound of her mother's voice.

" I think I must have fallen asleep," she murmured, more than a little confused.

Mrs Hampton dumped the pile of newly-ironed clothes on to a chair. " More need to be ironing your own clothes, my lass," she said, and paying no heed to Jennifer's quiet apology, she quickly crossed the room and pulled the curtains across the window, shutting the room off from the snowstorm.

"A blizzard in April." She sounded quite indignant. "I don't know what the weather is coming to !"

"I was lying watching it." Jennifer's tone was dull, as if the closing of the curtains had taken away something precious. It was beautiful, she wanted to add, but she was afraid that her resentment would sound in her voice and her mother would get angry again. And she couldn't bear the thought of another scene.

Mrs Hampton's snort indicated that she hadn't time to watch blizzards.

"It'll soon blow over, I expect," she said. "These unexpected storms never last for very long." She stopped at the door and turned. "Tea will be ready soon, so you might as well come and lay the table, after you've put away your clean clothes."

And the door closed behind her before Jennifer could answer.

Jennifer sat on the edge of the bed, rebellious and indignant, aware that her mother thought that she was sulking and was treating her accordingly, talking to her as if she were a petulant child who had been naughty and refused to admit it.

IT had all seemed perfectly all right yesterday afternoon when Michael Dryden had asked her to go to the pictures.

"Shall we go straight from the office?" he had suggested. "We could have a bite to eat first."

"Well," she had hesitated, "I'd have to let my mother know. I could phone our next-door neighbour, but she may not be in." Aware of her burning cheeks, she hadn't quite known how to handle the situation, especially when she saw that Anne and Lesley were casting speculative glances at her as they waited for the lift.

"All right." Michael, too, had noticed that the other girls were watching and waiting. "I'll come by your office in about half an hour, if you nod I'll know it's settled and I'll wait for you outside at six o'clock."

"Yes, all right," Jennifer had answered breathlessly and without looking at him again she'd hurried to catch up with her friends.

They were only supposed to have a ten-minute tea break, but for once Jennifer took an extra few minutes to make her telephone call. Mrs Graham said she'd willingly pass on Jennifer's message, and she replaced the receiver with a sigh of relief.

I expect I'd have spent the afternoon worrying instead of day-dreaming if I'd known how much trouble that telephone call would cause, she thought now.

"Goodnight, then." Michael had kept hold of her hand when they arrived at her garden gate. "I'll see you at the youth club tomorrow night."

There had been a wistful longing in his voice, as if tomorrow was an eternity away.

"Yes." Jennifer drew her hand away from his, sure that her racing heartbeats would be echoing right through to her fingertips. She ought to thank him, say something, anything, but her voice seemed to have disappeared.

" Well . . ." Michael pushed his hands into his pockets and stared down at the ground, kicking at a piece of gravel.

And then the porch light had come on, flowing over them like a shower of cold water. The door opened, and above the sound of empty milk bottles came her father's voice.

" Is that you, Jennifer?"

" Goodnight, and thank you." Her words had been almost drowned by the creak of the garden gate, and she'd hurried along the path and into the house.

" And where have you been, miss?" Her father's voice seemed loud and harsh.

" We've been worried to death." Her mother's tone was angry and accusing.

" I was at the pictures with a boy from the office," Jennifer stammered. " I phoned Mrs Graham. She said she'd let you know."

" Oh, she let us know you weren't to be in for tea all right," Mrs Hampton said, " but we didn't know where you were," she added. " Nor who you were with until this time of night."

Jennifer glanced at the clock, it was only ten to nine.

" I'm sorry, I thought it would be all right."

But an apology wasn't enough. She had to tell them all the details, that Michael was a boy who worked in the accounts department at the office, that she had met him at the youth club, that he lived only a few streets away and that he played football in one of the junior teams.

At the mention of football Jennifer was relieved to find a lightening of the atmosphere, for her brother, Alan, came to her aid by saying that he knew Michael and telling her parents how good a right-winger he was.

Jennifer relaxed a little, noticing that her father's eyes were gradually moving back to the television screen, and then her mother finally rose to her feet.

" Well, we might as well have a cup of tea," she'd said, and Jennifer had known that the row was over.

Now she hung away the last of her clothes, wondering if Alan had deliberately talked too much in order to distract her parents. You could never tell with Alan, she reflected, he was a very self-contained type of person, and, although he was only two years her senior and therefore closest to her in the family, she often thought that the only link between them was the fact that they were the only two who were still unmarried and living at home.

BEFORE she went downstairs she smoothed out the crushed counterpane on her bed and fluffed up the pillow, finding herself gazing wistfully at the other bed in the room. She missed the company of Audrey, who had been married for almost four months. And then she bit her lip, recalling how miserable Audrey had been when Margaret, their eldest sister, got married.

"You're too young to understand," Audrey had told Jennifer then. "I don't grudge Margaret her happiness, it's just that I'll have nobody to talk to, nobody really on my side." She'd sighed heavily. "And Mum will always be on at me about what time I come home and about the clothes I wear."

Jennifer closed the bedroom door behind her and went downstairs, remembering that without Margaret as mediator there had always seemed to be sparks flying between Audrey and her mother. The wedding preparations had certainly put a stop to all the rows and the house was much quieter these days. And Jennifer realised that it had been silly of her to wish that she had Audrey to confide in, for she knew too well what her advice would have been.

"You want to stand up for yourself! Just tell Mum that you're old enough to live your own life!"

IN the kitchen Mrs Hampton was busy at the cooker, but she looked up with a smile when Jennifer entered.

"Almost ready," she said. "I think that's Alan coming in now. I expect he'll be like a snowman. Silly to play football on a day like this. Still," she added, "I'm glad none of us will be going out again tonight for the storm is worse than ever."

Jennifer drew in a breath, feeling her nervous heart fluttering against her ribs.

I'll be going out, she wanted to say. I'm meeting Michael at the youth club.

But the thought refused to put itself into words, and her throat burned with the knowledge that this was the way it always was. Faced with a strong opinion, she was always too timid to express her own point of view. Countless numbers of times her mind had been firmly made up, her decision secure, only to crumble in the face of someone else's disapproval.

Like the time she had been going to wear her pink trouser-suit to the school dance and her mother had insisted on her wearing a long dress. The evening had been a disaster because trouser-suits or mini dresses were in fashion that year. Then there was the time she'd been swotting up her maths the night before an exam, and Audrey had dragged the book from her hand, saying that the night before was too late for swotting. She'd failed that exam through letting Audrey get away with being so bossy.

They meant well, she knew that. And she told herself that she didn't like to hurt their feelings by going against their advice. But she knew in her heart that she was just too timid, too much of a coward to have to argue or fight for the right to make her own decisions.

With shaking fingers she set out the cutlery, thinking of these other occasions and her own irritation with herself. But she knew now that these failures to assert herself had been unimportant in themselves. Only now, she realised with an aching regret, only now when I'm on the threshold of a whole new world, when I've fallen in love with the most wonderful boy in the world, only now is it truly important to be brave.

Mrs Hampton was aware of her daughter's misery, and knew that there was nothing she could say that would help. Of course, she told herself, it's a good thing it was nipped in the bud, for seventeen is far too young for boy friends. All right for some girls, but not for Jennifer, she's too shy, too unsure of herself. Now that she has started going to the youth club she'll come out of her shell, gain some confidence through mixing with other young folk . . . With a sigh, Mrs Hampton hoped that the disastrous date last night wouldn't make the poor lass even less confident.

She was genuinely sorry that Jennifer had been given such an angry welcome home last night, especially when it turned out that there had been no need to worry, but a mother couldn't help worrying and fussing, it was part of nature. And it had all been forgotten by bed-time . . . until that awful moment when Alan had said that he was staying up to watch the late movie on television.

" It's a horror film." He'd rubbed his hands with glee, and then asked Jennifer jokingly, " I don't suppose it was the horror film at the Regal you saw tonight, was it?"

" Yes, it was the Regal we went to." Jennifer's voice had trembled, and then she'd fled upstairs as if she were ready to burst into tears.

" Oh, my word." Mrs Hampton had stared at the other two in dismay.

Afterwards she had gone up to Jennifer's bedroom to say goodnight. " Never mind, love, you've plenty of time for dates. There'll be other chances," she'd said consolingly.

THE two men took their second cups of tea through to the living-room so that they could watch television, and Jennifer and her mother sat together in silence until Mrs Hampton rose from the table with a sigh. She put some dishes on the draining board, glancing out of the window at the blizzard. And when she turned back to the table there was loving concern in her voice.

" What a pity it's such a bad night . . . the youth club would have cheered you up."

" I won't let the weather stop me. I promised to meet Michael."

To her surprise, her voice was firm and controlled, but her heart was thudding as she waited for her mother's reaction.

Mrs Hampton's eyes widened in surprise.

" But I thought . . ." She hesitated. " I mean, I thought you said . . ."

Jennifer stared at her, feeling almost let down that her mother didn't seem to notice she had asserted herself, had spoken out against her mother's decision.

" I mean," Mrs Hampton said unsteadily, " you said he took you to see that horror film."

" Oh." The colour came and went in the girl's cheeks, and her lips curved into a smile. " But that was all right. He noticed that I was scared so we came out before it got too terrible."

" I thought that you were upset because . . ." Mrs Hampton stopped.

Jennifer bit her lip, but she forced herself to speak.

" No, I was upset because you and Dad were so angry." She took a deep breath. " I didn't think you'd mind me phoning next door, and I wasn't late home at all . . . and you made . . ."

" Such a fuss," her mother finished wryly. " I was sorry about that, Jennifer. With you being the baby of the family, I'm inclined to forget that you're growing up, and "—she hesitated—" old enough to have a boy friend."

" He's a nice boy, Mum."

" I'm glad." Mrs Hampton smiled at her daughter as if to say that it wasn't only the fact that the boy was so nice that made her glad, it was the knowledge that she and Jennifer had come closer to understanding each other.

S O I have to go and meet him tonight." Jennifer's voice interrupted her thoughts.

" But it's a terrible night," Mrs Hampton protested, half-turning towards the window. " But it's up to you. If your mind's made up I can't stop you."

Jennifer put her hand to her mouth to stifle a nervous giggle.

" Oh, Mum," she said, " you know I always do what you say ! I never argue." Her voice trembled between tears and laughter.

" The easiest way out. But not when it comes to something important, is that it?"

" I'm an awful coward."

" Nonsense," her mother answered briskly. " You're just like your dad, you don't like an argument, if it means hurting somebody's feelings. But he actually isn't a coward, I've never known him to shirk anything unpleasant. It was a bit of a thought to him to go and complain about that bad repair job on the car yesterday, but he went, because he knew that he was in the right. And then there was the time he saw smoke coming out of a window and broke in and rescued the three little children."

Jennifer listened in silence. She had heard the stories before, but now she was realising that there was more to her parents than just the fact that they were her mum and dad. They were individual people, with their own hopes and fears. Each of them had a different personality, but they must have learned to live in harmony so that their home had always been a happy one.

Thinking of happiness made her think of Michael. It was time to get dressed for going to the youth club. There was always dancing on a Saturday night, and she could just imagine herself in Michael's arms. The lights would be dim, and maybe there would be a slow, dreamy waltz, she thought with a delicious thrill of anticipation.

Outside, the whole town was white and shimmering. The blizzard had blown itself out, and the dark sky twinkled with a myriad of stars. Jennifer pulled the hood of her jacket back and shook out her light hair, lifting her face up to breathe in the pure fresh air as she walked lightly down the garden path. And then as she reached the gate a dark figure detached itself from the shadowy trees, and as her grip tightened on

The People's Friend Annual

the gate in momentary panic, her first instinct was to fly back into the safety of the house.

" Jennifer? It's me, Michael," his reassuring voice came in the same instant. " I came along . . . just in case . . ." He sounded hesitant, unsure of himself.

Under the street lamp Jennifer saw that he was nervous and ill at ease, like a lost little boy, and she smiled. It was up to her to reassure him now.

" I had to have a bit of an argument with Mum," she said brightly. " She thought it was silly to go out on a night like this. But I knew you'd be at the youth club. And, anyhow, the blizzard has stopped now."

" Yes." He brushed at a few snowflakes on his shoulder. " I caught the last of it, I think."

They began to walk along in the direction of the club, their feet making little crunching noises in the powdery snow.

She looked at him, answering his smile and glowing in the radiance of the starlit evening. They walked slowly, not even holding hands, and the silence between them was a token of their new-found love, which had no need of words.

Already the snow was melting on the pavements, dissolving in the branches of the trees, drying on the roofs of the houses. Soon the storm would be forgotten, it couldn't last, her mother had said.

And for a little while Jennifer had thought that her love for Michael would be the same, an unexpected storm of emotion which would soon be forgotten. But instead she had found the courage to stand up for herself, to insist on coming out to meet him tonight.

There was no guarantee that their love would last any longer than the storm. Maybe some day this wonderful moment would be no more than sweet memory. But nothing could take away the magic of this exquisite happiness of walking by his side, knowing that they had fallen in love.

Nature's bounty, reward for honest toil.

THREE'S A CROWD

by
Rona Melrose

K EN FARQUHARSON screwed up his face at the photograph he held in his hand.

"Do you think we're ever likely to run into Susan again?" he asked.

"If you hadn't encouraged her at the start, I don't suppose she would have hung around the way she did," his wife Charlotte replied snappily as she took the photograph from him and tried to make out what the blurred image represented.

"She's even managed to spoil this snapshot and it's the only one from this year's holiday that we have of the two of us."

"You sound like a jealous woman, Charlotte!" Ken said half-teasingly. Then suddenly he seemed to wonder if perhaps there could be a grain of truth in what he'd said.

The People's Friend Annual

"You don't mean . . . you really did feel jealous?" he asked in astonishment. "Why, that's ridiculous. Susan was at least four years older than I was."

"And I'm four years younger than you are, Ken! What does that prove?"

Yet, even as she said it, Charlotte reflected that, of course, she hadn't been jealous. She hadn't been altogether pleased at Ken giving so much attention to the other girl . . . woman.

She expected—wanted—all his attention to be on herself, and she couldn't help resenting any other outside attractions.

Susan Armitage, a mature thirty years against her own youthful twenty-two and Ken's twenty-six, had also seemed a more interesting person—and that was probably where the irritation started. And hadn't she been just a little mysterious, too?

There she'd been, travelling alone on a coach tour holiday to the Channel Isles, her long brown hair, quiet blue eyes and nice complexion making an attractive picture. *Miss* Susan Armitage.

CHARLOTTE'S thoughts wandered to the start of the holiday just over a month before.

The coach had left on its journey south from Edinburgh, but it was on the road between there and the Borders that they picked up Miss Armitage, along with several others. She and Ken, though, had been spared her company on the way down.

Almost half the coach party left the tour at Bournemouth. And after a flight by air across the Channel to the island of Jersey, the remainder scattered to the various hotels booked for them.

Susan Armitage had registered at their hotel and was sitting at their table when they went down to breakfast next morning.

They'd smiled politely and exchanged the usual pleasantries, but Ken had been the one to encourage the conversation further.

"Have you been to Jersey before, Susan?" he inquired warmly.

"No, this is my first time," she told them. "My elder sister was to have come with me, but she fell ill only a few days before we were due to leave. I didn't much like the idea of holidaying on my own, so I was going to cancel the tour. But my sister insisted I go without her. She said she knew how much I'd been looking forward to it, and that she'd get almost as much enjoyment listening to me tell her about it when I got back."

Susan Armitage didn't need much encouragement to talk. All the more reason, Charlotte felt, why Ken didn't have to lead her on as much as he did.

Charlotte talked, too, of course. But when she mentioned Ken and herself she could see Susan look at her, then at Ken, and back again, as if critically appraising the sort of couple they made. Charlotte, resenting this, felt the more annoyed.

Ken, on the other hand, didn't seem to see anything wrong, and when Susan started on about "regretting being persuaded to come to Jersey on my own," he straightaway invited her to join them on the trip to St Helier they'd planned.

128

Of course, he turned for her approval first, but after the enthusiastic way he had issued the invitation, what could she say?

LOOKING back, Charlotte couldn't really say Susan's company wasn't enjoyable. She succeeded in making the visit far more interesting than it might otherwise have been.

She'd read all she could about the island, she'd told them, and was able to fill them in on lots of background information.

But next morning, when they prepared to join the coach outside their hotel for an all-day tour of the island, Susan Armitage was there, too. She'd decided at the last moment that the same idea appealed to her.

And the morning after that she came up to them in the hotel foyer.

" Would you like to come with me to St Brelade's Bay, to see the Festival of Flowers? " she asked.

" I've heard it's a marvellous spectacle—something you shouldn't miss."

Actually, Ken had talked about going for a swim, and Charlotte had been keen on the idea, especially as the weather that morning was so perfect.

But Ken had fallen over himself to accept Susan Armitage's alternative suggestion.

" She's right, you know, Charlotte," he said. " If we don't see the fete today we won't get another chance this holiday. There'll be other days for the beach, sweetheart."

The " sweetheart " bit, she knew, was only an added inducement to get her to agree.

And, of course, she had. Moreover, the fete had been a really spectacular occasion, with flower-decorated floats in a rainbow colour of blooms and designs. A band had given an added touch of excitement and jollity to the proceedings, giving out gay and cheerful music, which sounded along all the hot, sunny side streets as they passed.

The next day was just as perfect for swimming. Some of the other guests from the hotel had the same idea, and a short bus run took them all into St Helier—Susan Armitage among them, of course.

" It looks as though I'm never going to get you to myself on this holiday, Ken," Charlotte complained as they straggled along behind the others in the direction of the beach.

He was obviously surprised, as if he had no idea she felt like that. Then, while the others strolled on, Ken stopped.

" If that's what you want, Charlotte, we'll slip away now, while Susan keeps everybody occupied. This street here should lead us to another part of the beach."

They soon found exactly the spot they'd been looking for. Charlotte had never enjoyed sea bathing so much. The water had been shallow, and, of course, warm, with a bright sun. To stretch out on the sand afterwards was sheer bliss.

But as she raised her head for a moment to look around, her eyes fastened on a now familiar figure, and she realised that Susan's keen eyes must have spotted Ken and herself before she turned away.

Somehow, sitting there all on her own, Charlotte couldn't help but reflect that she made a slightly pathetic figure.

" I'm sure she saw us, Ken," she told her husband.

" But why doesn't she come over and speak? And what's happened to those folk she was with when we left her?"

" I suppose they must have done the same as ourselves—slipped off when they saw an opportunity. She's looking this way again. Oh, but she turned her head away when I smiled at her. I've a feeling we've offended her."

Charlotte felt guiltily unhappy.

" I'm the one to blame if we have, Ken. But what can we do about it now?"

" Come on," Ken said decisively.

T HEY walked over in Susan's direction.

" Hello," Ken said. " Didn't you notice us then?"

" Well, yes," Susan replied hesitantly, " but I was afraid you would think I was forcing my company on you too much."

" But that's silly !" Charlotte assured her, though not without an embarrassed blush that Susan should guess so near to the truth.

" I thought I'd like to take a photograph," Ken said.

" One of you and Charlotte . . . to remind us of the holiday."

" Oh, yes, well all right, and perhaps I could take one of you and Charlotte together, afterwards?" Susan suggested eagerly.

And now Charlotte was handing that very snapshot back to her husband.

" Susan must have been shaking all over when she took this," he remarked, laughing as he looked at it again.

" Do you think she was pleased to feel we were at last showing an interest? I wonder what she really thought of us?"

Charlotte recalled clearly the time for parting from their holiday friend. When Susan left the coach at the homeward stopping place, Charlotte had overheard the beginning of a conversation between Susan and an older woman who met her — her sister, she guessed.

The words of the two

FROM NEAR HIS HEART

I OFTEN tell this lovely tale to bridal couples. Of an ancient Bible which had two verses in Genesis marked.

They tell how God removed a rib from Adam and created Eve therefrom.

And the same hand that set a cross against these verses had written at the foot of the page:

" Eve was not taken from Adam's head: that she might rule over him.

Eve was not taken from Adam's foot: that he might trample her beneath him.

But Eve was taken from Adam's side; to be his companion for life.

She was taken from near his heart; that he might cherish her all his days."

Rev. T. R. S. Campbell

women had carried through the half-open side window of the coach.

" And did you have a nice holiday, Susan?"

" It was lovely, Elizabeth. Just as you said it would be. I met the nicest young couple on the trip. They took me with them everywhere they went . . ."

For a moment Charlotte had felt ashamed. Her meanness at the start of the holiday came back to her.

Then she smiled and felt warm again, for hadn't she—with Ken's help, of course—overcome her unworthy thoughts?

It was good to know that the love she so much cherished—her love for Ken, her husband, which she'd so nearly marred by her possessiveness—had instead reached out to warm the heart of even one lonely person.

AYE HER FATHER'S GIRL

THATCHED cottages gleamed white in the sunshine as Sue MacGregor drove swiftly through the village of Fortingall. She had left Aunt Maisie's home in Glasgow very early this morning, so that she would arrive bright and early at her parents' farm just outside Aberfeldy.

And now her head was bursting with all the questions she wanted to ask them.

Why, for instance, hadn't they told her that she wasn't their own child and had been adopted at birth?

Why had they left it to chance that Aunt Maisie might tell her suddenly as she had done last night?

It was as she was driving into Aberfeldy past a friendly policeman who waved to her that Sue's courage had suddenly deserted her.

" I can't face them yet. I can't," she cried aloud.

In something like panic she had crossed the bridge across the Tay and turned west towards the haven of Glen Lyon where she had spent so many happy hours.

Eventually, as she grew calmer, Sue stopped the car and got out to gaze down the narrow glen where the crystal-clear water sped busily over the rocky floor of the river.

She had always loved this spot and now, in late summer, with the trees gently turning yellow and the sun burnishing the mossy bank so that it looked like copper, the sight gave her a special pang.

" This is the loveliest time of the year. Father always says . . ."

Only he isn't really my father, Sue reminded herself. But why didn't he tell me? I've always believed in him, and even modelled myself on him. What can I believe in now?

Ever since she could remember, Sue had adored her giant of a father. When she was young he would put her astride his horse and take her with him wherever he went. He taught her to ride and, when she was old enough, taught her everything he knew about cars.

" It's time you stopped treating her as if she were a boy ! There are other things she should be learning !" her mother would protest.

But Sue and her father were firm friends. When her schooldays were over she came to work on the farm, against her mother's wishes.

Then early last winter, shortly after Sue's nineteenth birthday, the peace was abruptly shattered. Aunt Maisie's husband died suddenly, and she wrote begging Sue to spend a month or so with her after the funeral.

Mrs MacGregor sighed when she read the letter.

by Dorothy Wright

132

" Poor Maisie, I do feel we ought to help her at a time like this . . .

" I'd go myself," Mrs MacGregor went on, " but there's so much to do just now and this year we are expecting one or two holiday guests."

" Oh, I could cope with all that !" Sue interrupted a bit too eagerly. " After all, Mum, she is your only sister. Oh, please ! You know what Aunt Maisie's like when she gets me to Glasgow. She always finds some excuse to keep me there !"

MRS MACGREGOR turned to her husband, her mouth set in a determined line.

" John," she asked, " why don't you say something?"

Mr MacGregor put down his paper and looked from one to the other.

" I can't see how I'm going to manage without either of you," he began tactfully, " but I suppose someone will have to help Maisie or we'll never hear the last of it."

He paused for what seemed ages before he made his decision.

" Och, it'll have to be you, Sue. With her rheumatism, you know your aunt never walks a step if she can help it, and since your mother can't drive . . ."

Mr MacGregor touched his daughter's shoulder.

" Cheer up, Sue. A month isn't for ever."

B UT many months had gone by. Looking back, Sue could hardly believe how time had flown.

And if it hadn't been for Hugh it never would have, she told herself.

She'd met Hugh Collier almost the first week she'd been in Glasgow. He worked in the offices of Bruce, MacWhirter & White, her aunt's accountants.

Sue had driven Aunt Maisie for an appointment with old Mr Mac-Whirter and was left waiting in the outer office. For want of something better to do, and perhaps because her thoughts were never far from home, she helped herself to a scribbling pad left lying on the desk and began to sketch some of the birds and plants to be found back home.

When a tall, slim young man burst into the office she looked up guiltily.

" Sorry to keep you waiting," he said.

" Waiting?"

" I'm Hugh Collier. Is that a message you're writing on my pad?"

" No. Oh, I'm sorry! I've been doodling. It's a habit of mine when I've nothing else to do. I suppose I've no right to be sitting at your desk, but Mr MacWhirter . . ."

" Oh, that's all right. I never leave anything confidential lying around." He grinned and picked up the pad. " Isn't that a plover?"

" Oyster catcher, same family."

" Of course! The truth is, I don't really know much about birds. But these look great to me. Are you a naturalist?"

" Goodness, no! Unless you include working on my father's farm. At the moment I'm staying with my aunt, she's in the inner sanctum just now with your Mr MacWhirter."

" Where did you learn to draw like this?"

" Learn? I didn't."

" Must be a gift then. One of your parents?"

" My father's a man of action. I don't think I've ever seen him sit long enough to do anything like drawing." Her eyes gleamed with pride. " And Mum doesn't draw either, but she's always encouraging me. Says it's a more ladylike pursuit than driving a tractor! You see, I take after my father, I like to be doing things. This, as I said before, is just doodling."

Sue tore the leaf from the pad and was about to crumple it in her hands when Hugh stopped her.

" Pretty good doodling! Mind if I keep it? I'd like to show it to a friend of mine. He runs a small group at his house for young folk, and in fine weather they go out into the parks to draw and paint."

" Have it by all means, though I can't see what good it will do. I'm only here on a short visit, so I'm not likely to be joining your friend's group !"

And she never would have but for Aunt Maisie's accident. The day it happened, her aunt's rheumatism had been playing her up rather badly. Her ankles were so swollen she could scarcely move, but she suddenly had the idea that a walk might do them some good.

It was the last day Sue would have chosen for walking, the pavements were so damp and slippery. But she'd had a brief note from her father that morning saying they were short-handed and asking when he could expect her home.

She showed the note to her aunt just before they set out for the walk, and, though Aunt Maisie seemed put out at the prospect of losing Sue quite so soon, she had grudgingly agreed to let her return home at the weekend.

IT wasn't until they were almost home that Aunt Maisie suddenly remembered she'd meant to buy a box of her favourite peppermints from the sweet shop on the corner.

" I'll go back," Sue volunteered, " just as soon as I've helped you up to the flat."

" Anyone would think I was an old woman !" her aunt snapped. " I can look after myself. I always have done, haven't I?"

" Then why am I here?" Sue longed to ask. But, without a word, she left her aunt and hurried off to the sweet shop. When she returned a few minutes later she found Aunt Maisie lying on the shop floor, her right leg doubled up under her and poor Miss Tweedie, the assistant, on the verge of hysterics.

" The mat !" Miss Tweedie gasped. " She slipped on the mat !"

While Aunt Maisie's leg was being X-rayed and put into plaster, Sue rang her father.

" What shall I do?" she asked.

" A fractured leg? Sounds a long job to me, Sue. No, no, you don't have to worry about things up here, we can manage fine."

There was a crackle on the line and she heard him say something about " duty."

" Ay, but if you should be wanting to come home, can you not get someone to look after your aunt? She won't mind the cost. But it's up to you."

Sue hesitated. The suggestion seemed like a lifeline and she was ready to grasp it when she remembered her father set little store by anyone who shirked their duty, and seemingly this was her duty.

" Maybe I'd better stay, Father. For a while, anyway," she said, and was rewarded with a grunt of satisfaction.

Fortunately a much more mellow Aunt Maisie returned from the hospital and she seemed almost shamefaced about her accident.

" Now you're not to spend all your time up here with me. You've got your car, so go home occasionally. Miss Tweedie can always stay sometimes to keep me company, and between times get out, meet some young folk."

Sue knew she couldn't say that all she longed to do was to be climbing Ben Lawers or fishing for salmon in the Tay. Maybe just wandering under the birks of Aberfeldy.

She looked out of the window as if she were trying to make up her mind. The pavements below were saturated with driving rain, and people scurried by as if they hadn't a moment to spare. And here I am with far too much time, she thought. Looking after Aunt Maisie will never keep me fully occupied. Idly, she started to trace the outline of a bird on the damp window-pane.

S UE ! What are you drawing?"
" Oh, it's just . . ."
She swung around, suddenly remembering Hugh Collier and what he had said about his friend's group.

" Aunt Maisie, I know how I could meet some young people. I could take painting lessons !"

She was startled by her aunt's reaction. She stared at Sue as if she'd just announced she was about to take off for the moon, then she pointed to the portrait of the three sisters, which, as long as Sue could remember, had held pride of place over the mantelpiece.

" You mean you want to paint like that?"

" Oh, Aunt Maisie, how could I? I thought something more simple, birds and flowers, maybe in watercolours."

She walked across the room to study the portrait more closely. There was Maisie, the eldest, sitting straight-backed and grim-faced with Ann, Sue's mother, at her side, smiling self-consciously. And, in the foreground, looking straight at the artist with eyes that danced with amusement, was the youngest and prettiest, Fiona.

" Aunt Fiona looks so nice," Sue commented. " Imagine, only nineteen when she married, and twenty years old when she died."

Aunt Maisie came out of her trance.

" Now about those lessons of yours . . ."

Sue wondered why, even after all these years, both Aunt Maisie and her mother seemed reluctant to talk about their sister. Surely they couldn't still mourn her?

She had yet to learn that the young woman she referred to as Aunt Fiona was the mother who had given her birth, and that the artist had been Sue's father.

" I do know of someone who runs a small art group . . . he's a friend of Mr Collier, the young man in Mr MacWhirter's office." She looked down at her hands. " I was wondering whether he would let me join his classes."

" Ah, so you didn't waste your time in Mr MacWhirter's office that day?" her aunt teased. " And which is it you're really interested in, the lessons or young Mr Collier?"

Since that first meeting, Sue had thought a lot about Hugh. It was extraordinary. Back home she'd always lost interest in the boys she met as there never seemed to be one to measure up to her father.

Not that Hugh did, Sue sharply reminded herself as she waited for him to call. She'd already spoken to him over the telephone, and his surprise and pleasure at hearing her voice again had been quite flattering.

" There'll be no difficulty at all in joining the group," he'd said. " I've already shown your sketch to my friend Ken, and he was quite impressed. Tell you what, I'll call for you this evening and take you along there . . . No, no trouble at all."

Time never dragged when she was with Hugh. It was when Aunt Maisie started to get about and take over the reins of the business once more that she became bored.

Time was when she might have packed her bags and gone straight back to Aberfeldy, but the thought of saying goodbye to Hugh troubled her. The hours spent with him had become very precious.

But what did they mean to him? Would he miss her when she had gone? Would he make the effort to see her again? He never said.

THE opportunity to find out came one day when Sue heard from her father that his sister, Kate, was coming over from America to pay them a visit. He hadn't seen Kate for almost twenty years, and, naturally, wanted Sue to be home to meet her.

" You'll come back, won't you?" Aunt Maisie said when Sue told her.

" If you really need me I'll come back," Sue promised.

At that moment she'd have said anything. She'd just invited Hugh to spend a few days with her while Aunt Kate was over and was up in the clouds now that he had accepted.

" From all you've told me I gather your father's quite a hero, Sue. I'm looking forward to meeting him."

But had she detected just a shade of anxiety in his voice she wondered, the night before she was due to leave for Aberfeldy?

She'd already said goodnight to her aunt, but she came wandering into Sue's bedroom on some pretext or other.

" Be sure to tell Kate she's welcome here if she comes to Glasgow."

" I'll give her your message," she said. She closed the suitcase and looked at her aunt. " It's going to seem strange to Father, seeing his sister again after all these years. I wonder what she looks like?"

" The image of your father, by all accounts !"

" I suppose it'll be like looking at myself in middle-age !"

" And how can that be when you're not even related?"

Sue swung around as if she'd been struck, to see the anger had ebbed from her aunt's face.

"Not even related? How can that be? She's my father's sister, isn't she?"

" I'd no right to say that, Sue. It wasn't for me . . ."

" But you have, so you owe me an explanation !"

" It's time you knew anyway," Aunt Maisie said wearily. " John and Ann couldn't have children of their own, so they adopted you when Fiona died."

" Fiona? She's my mother? So my father is the artist."

" Jared Forbes was a steel engraver," her aunt corrected, " but he liked to paint."

" Why didn't they tell me?" Sue kept saying.

SUE couldn't remember how long she'd been standing by the river when Hugh found her.

He took her in his arms and she didn't resist him.

" How did you find me?"

" I asked a policeman ! Apparently your car's well known ! Come on, Sue, come home, your folk are worrying about you. When I arrived before you, we all thought something must have happened."

" You met my father?" she asked.

" And your mother, and Aunt Kate." He laughed. " You know, Sue, I believe she's more American than the Americans !"

She didn't answer. There seemed no point. He shook her gently.

" I'm trying to tell you that she's adapted herself to her environment. It isn't only a question of heredity, it's mannerisms, a way of speech, little things. I've only just met your father, but you're his daughter."

" If only he'd told me," she kept saying.

" Let's accept the fact that, for once in his life, he made a mistake, a bad one. Are you going to hold it against him ? "

" It isn't like that, Hugh. I . . . I'm scared. It's like going to meet a stranger. I don't know what I'm going to say when I see him again."

" I know exactly how you feel. Felt that way myself until a short while ago. I thought, How am I going to tell this superman that I love his daughter and want to marry her ? "

" You really mean that?"

" Can you doubt it?" He held her tight as if he'd never let her go. " Come on, Sue, let's find him. You've got to face the fact that he's really only human. He makes mistakes like the rest of us.

" Let's go," he whispered. " It's you who needs to be strong now."

This is my home, hard would it be to leave.

A FRIEND IN NEED

BY AILEEN MITCHELL

THE semi-circle of white-clad angels stood near the piano, waiting for their opening chord. In front of them, Miss Strachan, who was responsible for the success of the school's nativity tableau, stood tense and anxious. Dress rehearsals were famed for their mishaps, and today's run-through had gone true to form.

Joseph had lost his beard, Herod had forgotten his words, and one of the three kings had made an impressive entrance by tripping over his cloak and landing full-length on the floor.

Helen Strachan lifted her arms and led the childish voices into chorus. " *Glory to God on high, Praise to the new-born King . . .* "

For a moment Helen felt her heart swell with the fervour and sweetness of the singing. Whatever else had gone wrong, the angels with their snowy dresses and golden halos were in every way right.

And then her glance fell on the second angel on the left.

Her arms dropped suddenly and the chorus petered out as twenty pairs of eyes looked at her speculatively.

She pointed at the angel who had caught her attention.

" Step out, please," she demanded. The child obeyed, alarm clouding her blue eyes.

" You're the new pupil, aren't you, from Miss Fraser's class?" Helen's voice was tense with strain and fatigue.

" Yes, miss," the child replied promptly. " My name is Betty Steele, miss."

" Well, Betty "—Helen spoke with annoyance—" can you imagine any angel wearing such a dirty dress?"

Betty looked down at her dress, biting her lip as she tried to cover the worst of the dirty marks with her hands. She lifted her head slowly.

" No, miss," she whispered.

Helen drew in her breath impatiently. All the irritations of the day seemed to overwhelm her at once, but she tried to control her feelings. It probably wasn't the child's fault, she told herself. Surely Mrs Steele could show a little more interest and see that the girl was turned out well.

" What can your mother be thinking about?" she said, echoing her thoughts. " Please tell her to have the dress properly washed and ironed for Wednesday's performance."

Betty stepped back into line, looking subdued, and Helen played the final chorus once again. This time the angels sang joyfully right through the carol, and Helen felt relieved and more hopeful as she dismissed the children.

" You mustn't worry." The headmistress had come into the hall and was looking anxiously at the flush on Helen's face. " Everything will be fine on Monday." She hesitated. There was more wrong with Helen than worry over the concert. " Will you be going away for Christmas?"

Helen shook her head.

" I shall be staying in the flat," she replied, and refused to be drawn any further.

BUT as Helen made her way home past the shops, gaily lit and decorated for the festive season, she had to admit that the thought of spending Christmas and the New Year alone was depressing her. Why did people assume that one had to be old to be lonely? She wasn't thirty-five, yet, when the walls of her flat closed around her in the evening, she was as much alone as if she were a hermit on a desert island. And it was when the family festivals came around that she felt her loneliness most keenly.

As she climbed the stairs to her front door and lit the gas fire in her sitting-room, Helen wondered again if she had been wise to leave the little Border town where she had been born and bred for Glasgow. And yet it had seemed the only thing to do when her parents had died. She had been tied for so many years, and, although she loved her home town, it held memories which were bitter as well as sweet.

It reminded her of Alec, who had loved her when she was twenty but who had another dream, too.

" Come to Canada," he had urged. " We'll have a wonderful life there."
But she was an only child, born late in life to parents who were now elderly.

" I can't leave them," she told Alec. " If you truly loved me you would understand."

The reproach in her eyes wasn't enough to still the restlessness for adventure which stirred him. He left, believing that she would follow, but her mother fell ill, making the decision even more difficult. Helen's love for Alec was as strong as ever, but misunderstandings are easy when people are separated by so many thousands of miles, and after a while their letters stopped. Finally, Helen heard that Alec was making a big success of the small business he had established and that he had married a local girl.

She could still feel the pain the news had given her, and simple incidents could still bring it back, unexpectedly and vividly.

That child today, for instance. Her eyes had been the same clear blue as Alec's. Helen felt guilty as she remembered the alarm that had sprung in them.

Perhaps she had been too sharp with her. Perhaps if she herself had a child like Betty her words would have been softer and kinder, because Christmas and Hogmanay would be occasions to look forward to and plan for. She wouldn't send her to school in a dirty dress, though, she thought, and bristled with indignation at Mrs Steele's carelessness.

AT that moment little Betty Steele was scrubbing away at the stains on her dress. She bit her lip and tears welled into her eyes as the stubborn marks refused to be budged. She wanted to wash the dress herself, because Daddy had told her that she mustn't ask Mrs Duncan to do too much for her.

" It is very kind of her to look after us," he had explained. " We must try not to be any trouble."

So when Betty had fallen down yesterday she had only tried to sponge the muddy stains off. Unfortunately, the result was worse than ever. She had hoped that the teacher wouldn't notice, but the memory of her stinging words still hurt as the child rubbed away.

" You're very busy this evening !" Richard Steele stood at the bathroom door, but the smile on his face faded as his little daughter turned and he noticed the tear-stains on her cheeks.

" Miss Strachan was horrid," she explained. " She said no angel would wear such a dirty dress and that my mother should have washed and ironed it properly."

Two soapy hands flung themselves around Richard Steele's neck and Betty buried her head in his shoulders as she cried again for the mother who had died two years previously when she was five.

For a moment anger for the teacher who had spoken such rough words bristled inside Richard, but as he comforted his daughter his shoulders drooped with silent resignation. This was just another of the difficulties which were constantly cropping up. It wasn't easy to bring up a child without a woman's help.

" Let's go downstairs and see what Mrs Duncan has for us," he suggested. " I thought I could smell hot-pot when I opened the door."

Betty dried her eyes thoughtfully.

" I don't like my teacher," she announced with determination. " I don't like her one little bit."

Neither do I, Richard thought grimly as he knocked on Mrs Duncan's kitchen door. And when I see you, Miss Strachan, I shall have something to say to you.

MRS DUNCAN was full of sympathy when she heard about Betty's difficulties.

" Just let me get hold of that teacher," she exclaimed indignantly. " Fancy upsetting the child so !"

She took charge of the dress, and by Wednesday it was bleached, boiled and ironed. Betty really looked an angel, dressed in sparkling white with her long, golden curls falling over her shoulders beneath her shining halo. Richard looked at her with pride as she stood second from the left on the stage, and he also scrutinised the teachers, wondering which one he had to tackle.

Helen stood in the wings, and felt relief flood over her as the tableau proceeded without hitch. The shepherds remembered their lines and their gifts, the innkeeper's humour was well appreciated by the audience, and the choir sang as if it were really composed of angels from heaven. Helen noticed particularly the little angel who stood second from the left. She saw with approval the beautifully-laundered dress, and made up her mind to give the child a small word of praise after the performance.

First, however, she found herself drawn on to the stage to acknowledge the response of the audience.

" I am sure," she heard the headmistress point out, " that you will all want to show appreciation to Miss Strachan who devised the tableau and has worked so hard to make tonight's performance possible."

So that's her ! Richard's jaw tightened and his hands lay clenched in his lap as the parents surrounding him clapped loudly. Well, he didn't want to make a scene, but he felt he should point out to Miss Strachan the danger of making snap judgments.

Helen was already talking to his daughter when Richard Steele approached.

" Your dress looks beautiful," she was saying. " Did you help your mummy wash it?"

Betty looked at her blankly and, as her father drew near, caught hold of his hand for comfort.

" I'm afraid you upset my little girl the other day," Richard began. " She has to do a great deal for herself as she has no mother to help her."

" I'm sorry . . ." Helen almost stammered.

" You must choose your words more carefully. Life isn't all that easy for Betty."

Richard's face was still grim as he put his arm around his daughter's shoulder and drew her away.

Helen felt glad that she could involve herself in the clearing up.

There was a lot to be done, and it helped to take the edge off her annoyance. Although her initial reaction had been one of remorse, Richard's uncompromising attitude had made her angry. Surely he should realise that with so many children to cater for it was impossible to know about each one's domestic circumstances. Maybe she had spoken sharply, but she was a teacher and had to maintain discipline. Suppose all the angels came to practice with dirty dresses? Would she have to conduct a survey into their family circumstances before reproving them?

Her thoughts continued to add fuel to her indignation when she returned to her flat, and until she fell asleep in the small hours. Next day her lonely breakfast was coloured by her irritation, and when she arrived at school she was glad to find Anne Fraser, Betty's teacher, in the staff-room. It was a relief to tell someone else about her encounter with Richard Steele.

" I think it most unfair of him to jump to conclusions without even hearing my side of the story," Helen finished angrily.

Anne raised her eyebrows.

" Calm down, Helen," she said soothingly. " You were in a state all that day, you may remember. Even the Head noticed it."

" But I said very little to the child," Helen replied defensively.

" Perhaps it was the way you said it," Anne suggested. " Nevertheless, don't worry about it. Mr Steele just wanted to get it off his chest, and he and Betty have probably forgotten all about it now."

HELEN made her way to the classroom feeling subdued. Anne's words made her look at the incident more objectively. There were excuses for her sharpness, she knew ; she had been tired, things had been going wrong, but she had hurt Betty, possibly bringing back the loss the child had suffered when her mother died.

At break she decided to visit the school secretary and find out Betty's address. She would send the child a Christmas card and perhaps write a short note wishing her well.

" Merry Christmas, miss !" The greeting was repeated thirty times at four o'clock

WITH EYES TO SEE

LIVE in Angus, you're by the gates of Paradise! None of Scotland's epic grandeurs here; but quiet loveliness at every turn.

Roads to dreaming hills, and canny roads to summer-scented howffs of peace. Autumn's golden glory over tree and field, and the swirling ribbons of the geese athward the winter sky. Blest the eye that sees such things!

Where is God found?

Go to the humble, consider the meek. Seek the thousand acts of loveliness that grace the face of ordinary life.

There is God found—as are found the glories of Angus.

Blest the eye that sees in modest, unobtrusive things the stirrings of the living God!

Rev. T. R. S. Campbell

as Helen's class left with glowing faces. Then she was alone in the classroom and the smile died from her face. A pile of little gifts from her pupils lay on her desk, and she scooped them up ruefully. She would open them on Christmas morning together with the few parcels which had already arrived from Braeburn.

She shivered slightly. Christmas by herself would be a new experience, and for a moment she was tempted to take the next train back to her home town. Several old friends would be glad to see her, but she shrugged the idea away firmly. She knew that her needs were deeper than just a desire for company. Caring for her sick parents had fulfilled her emotionally, but now they were no longer with her there was no one to care for or to need her.

T HE shopping fever of the next few days kept Helen occupied even though she only needed a few extra items. She bought a small chicken for her solitary Christmas dinner, some figs and dates, a few nuts and extra fruit and a small iced cake. Her shopping basket full, Helen stopped to gaze in the window of a toy shop, and thought of Betty. There were dolls of all sizes on display. Cuddly baby dolls, curly-haired dolls with frilly dresses, dark-haired, sophisticated dolls, dolls that walked and talked, dolls with extensive wardrobes. Suddenly Helen knew what she would do. Instead of just sending a Christmas card, she would buy Betty a doll and take it round to her on Christmas Eve.

The next half-hour was perhaps the most enjoyable Helen had spent for months. As she browsed around the toy shop she had difficulty not to empty her purse. Finally she settled for a pretty, flaxen-haired doll dressed in blue velvet. It was large enough to make a splendid gift, but not expensive enough for the Steeles to feel any embarrassment.

Helen returned to her flat well pleased with the afternoon's purchases, and after cooking a simple tea she found her writing pad and composed a short note to Betty. She tucked it inside the doll's box and then wrapped the present in a piece of gay paper.

Mrs Duncan's house was only a short walk from Helen's flat, and on Christmas Eve Helen was round there early. Not early enough, for the Steeles, however. They were already out shopping, and Mrs Duncan opened the door.

Helen gave her the parcel.

" This is a present for Betty. There is a note inside."

She turned quickly, almost before Mrs Duncan had finished thanking her. She was anxious to leave before the Steeles returned, for she had no wish to meet Richard Steele again.

Mrs Duncan put the parcel away and was glad for Betty. She herself had a large paintbox wrapped up and ready to give the child, and she knew Mr Steele had a few surprises in store, but no other gifts had been sent to the house.

She wondered who the stranger was, but when Richard Steele returned she was surprised to find that he was just as mystified.

" I can't think of anyone," he mused. " Betty must open it now so that we can find out who sent it."

The child needed no further prompting. Her eyes sparkled as she tore away the glittering paper, then she gasped with delight as she opened the box and saw the beautiful doll inside.

Her father picked up the note.

" It's from Miss Strachan !" he exclaimed.

Dear Betty, he read out. *I'm sorry if I upset you at the rehearsal, but your dress was beautiful for the tableau. I hope you enjoy a very happy Christmas. With best wishes, Helen Strachan.*

Betty replaced the doll thoughtfully.

" I still don't like Miss Strachan," she said firmly.

" But it's kind of her to send you such a lovely present," her father pointed out.

Betty put the lid on the box.

" Can we decorate the tree now, please, Daddy?"

" You must write to Miss Strachan to thank her." Richard spoke gently but firmly.

" Yes, Daddy, but I'd like to decorate the tree now."

She bounced out of the room, leaving the present on the table.

" You can't buy the affection of a child," Mrs Duncan commented. " Nevertheless, Miss Strachan seemed a very nice person. I'm sure she didn't mean to be unkind."

RICHARD STEELE followed his daughter upstairs and unpacked the decorations they had just bought. Betty could have her way over dressing the tree at the moment, but he would make sure she wrote later. He hoped she would do so willingly.

But it wasn't until Betty's bed-time that he mentioned the present again.

" Would you like to take your new doll to bed with you?" he suggested as he tucked the bedclothes around her shoulders.

" No, thank you," Betty replied firmly.

" She's going to be lonely shut up in her box all the time."

Betty hesitated.

" Let her sit on the chair by my bed," she suggested grudgingly. " She can watch for Santa Claus."

Richard placed the doll beside Betty's bed, and the child gently stroked the soft velvet of her dress.

" She's a pretty doll," she admitted. Then her face softened. " I'll call her Gillian."

Named, the doll was accepted and took her place in Betty's large family of assorted dolls and teddy bears.

" You'll write to Miss Strachan tomorrow," Richard reminded his daughter. " It was very kind of her to give you such a lovely gift."

On the following day the sitting-room was soon a jumble of tinsel and gay wrapping paper. Mrs Duncan joined in the celebrations, and in exchange for the paintbox Betty handed over a parcel containing a pair of gloves for which she had contributed quite a sum of her money.

Soon the aroma of roast turkey filled the small house, and when the pudding had been eaten and the crackers pulled, Richard brought out notepaper for Betty.

"Miss Strachan," he reminded her.

Betty nodded. She sucked her pencil for a moment, then disappeared into her bedroom. When she reappeared, she held an assortment of nuts, fruit and oddments.

"I want to give Miss Strachan a present, too," she said. "Can we take these to her if I wrap them up nicely?"

Richard hesitated. This would be an odd sort of present, but Betty's gesture was a generous one and he had the feeling that Miss Strachan would understand.

"A good idea," he agreed. "Even if Miss Strachan is out, a walk will do us both good."

WHILE Betty wrapped up her small gifts, Helen was drying the few dishes she had used for lunch. Her chores finished, she switched on the television and sank into a comfortable chair.

The ringing of the door bell suddenly startled her. She expected no one, but perhaps it was one of the pensioners who lived downstairs.

When she saw Richard Steele and his small daughter her eyes opened wide with surprise. Richard, too, found himself at a loss for words.

Betty saved the day.

"I've brought you a little present," she said, and handed over a small box containing the gaily-wrapped gifts.

Helen flushed with pleasure.

"Come away in," she invited.

Helen felt a lump come to her throat as she opened the carefully wrapped nuts, the orange, the bar of chocolate, the handful of sweets, the notebook. It was like having a Christmas stocking again.

Watching her delight as each small gift came into view, Richard wondered about Helen's life. Obviously she was spending Christmas alone.

Looking around, he saw Betty engrossed in a television programme.

"She's settled down."

He smiled, and Helen, noticing the way his eyes crinkled at the corners, wondered why she had ever found him aggressive.

"I'll get some coffee," she offered, and while she was in the kitchen she thought about the tinned fruit and cream and the Christmas cake stored away in the cupboard.

As she carried back the cups she felt light-hearted and happy, because she was sure of two things. She was going to ask her visitors to stay to tea, and she knew Richard would accept.

In distant days, Stirling was very much at the centre of the struggle for Scottish independence. The most famous of its battles was fought at near-by Bannockburn, and the young Mary, Queen of Scots, was crowned here after the death of her father. Rivalling the splendid Castle for the attention of every visitor is the starkly impressive Wallace Monument on a hillside to the north of the town.

Stirling

J. Campbell Kerr

JEAN BOOTH was missing her old neighbour more than she could say. She hadn't realised before just how much Mrs Riddock had shared in her everyday life. As she stood looking out of her window at the stretch of garden in front of her cottage where the first golden daffodil was lifting its head to the spring sunshine, she reflected that if Mrs Riddock had still been next door, she'd have been running in to tell her about the daffodil.

When her old neighbour had gone to live with her married daughter, Jean had hoped for pleasant people next door. It was all the more important because the two cottages, divided by a stone wall, were about half a mile from the country town of Karmuir and there was no other house at hand.

A lively family next door would have been wonderful. Jean had no brothers or sisters, and had always envied those who had. As a child she remembered repeatedly begging her parents for a little brother or sister for a birthday present and her intense disappointment when none

Her Not-So-Lazy Neighbour

by FRANCES WEIR

appeared. Now, at the age of thirty, she'd long taken a sensible view of the matter, but nevertheless she was surprised at the depth of her disappointment when the new tenant of the neighbouring cottage wasn't what she'd hoped for.

HE was middle-aged, unfriendly and a bit of an idler. Sometimes he lay in bed till nearly midday and often he prowled about till well after midnight. Jean had seldom seen him since he came, but the few glimpses she'd had hadn't impressed her favourably ; a lanky figure in shabby tweeds with a fringe of grey hair showing beneath his cloth cap, and a leonine look about his profile.

"Have you got to know Mr Foster yet ?" Penny Hamilton in the office would ask her often, but Jean had nothing to tell her.

" You should really ring his bell, you know," Penny advised. " A good neighbour always welcomes a stranger."

" I did ring his bell," Jean confessed. " The first day he moved in, but he didn't even answer it. He doesn't want to be friendly, I'm sure."

" Looks like it," Penny agreed. " I've heard he spends a lot of his time in town. He seems to be one of the idle rich, though he doesn't look like it.

" And he snoops around the country quite a bit," Penny added. " I've seen him going out with his van. I wonder what he's up to ?"

" I wonder," Jean echoed. " He'll just be filling in time, I suppose, but it seems a useless kind of life."

Today Jean had a busy morning in front of her, but she couldn't resist a quick visit to her solitary daffodil. She sniffed the fresh spring air appreciatively, then stooped to get a closer look at the perfectly formed golden-yellow bloom.

As she straightened, she glanced briefly at the upper windows next door. It was past ten and the shutters with which all the cottage windows were fitted were still closed. Sometimes they weren't open when she came home for lunch.

Jean was trying to break herself of the habit of looking up, which had started in Mrs Riddock's time, but it was difficult to stop. She couldn't help thinking of how her old neighbour, with all her disabilities, had always risen at seven. Jean sighed reminiscently as she hurried back to the house.

In the hall she paused in front of the mirror to sweep back the black waves of hair from her broad forehead. A pleasant reflection confronted her ; soft, rounded cheeks, a healthy colour and expressive dark eyes.

But she'd need to get on with her Saturday morning chores.

Fred Rae had promised to come up in the afternoon to start boarding in that tank in the living-room. Jean had been used to it from childhood, but it was rather an eyesore.

Fred and she had been friends since their schooldays and Jean wished with all her heart she could love him enough to marry him, but she just couldn't.

Dear, faithful Fred—she wasn't going to deceive either herself or him. She'd be an old maid and one day he'd find someone else to love.

At two o'clock Jean heard the sound of Fred's lorry trundling up the lane that led to the front of her house. She was at the door to greet him when he jumped out, a stock figure of medium size with sandy hair, clear grey eyes and a determined chin.

" Hello, Jean," he called out, his face lighting up at the sight of her.

" Hello, Fred," she responded cheerfully. " You're right on time."

" Have you ever seen me otherwise ?" he replied with a laugh. " Though I could mention a few folks who aren't."

It was a virtue he carried to excess, reflected Jean. Over the years it had become irritating, but then her more easy-going ways had very likely annoyed him.

Jean, doing some mending, watched the ugly tank disappear. Fred was unusually silent this afternoon, she reflected, but, of course, his mind was on the job. Nevertheless, she couldn't help feeling that something was worrying him, but he'd likely tell her in his own good time.

A T four o'clock Jean made Fred a cup of tea and he sat down thankfully. He seemed a bit abstracted and there wasn't the usual ease to his conversation.

" I see they've got a new assistant in Todd, the grocer's," Jean remarked. " She seems a very pleasant girl. She's served me more than once lately."

Fred was suddenly alert.

" I know," he said. " I've spoken to her."

Something in his tone made Jean give him a searching look, but she said nothing.

" She comes from the country," the young joiner went on, " and she's feeling a bit strange here."

He sounded and looked slightly embarrassed. Jean had never seen him like this before. Had he suddenly fallen in love with this pretty Marie Bowen ? A cold feeling struck at her heart, quite unreasonable, but there nevertheless. And what was this he was saying ?

"Jean, I've asked Marie to be my partner at the badminton dance. Maybe I should have asked you first, but you keep on telling me to go ahead and ask someone else and Marie told me she was lonely."

Jean swallowed hard. She should be glad, she told herself.

" Of course you're right," she managed to say in a forced voice. " Maybe you've found the right partner at last, Fred."

The young man shook his head rather dolefully.

" I'm not so sure about that, Jean, but I think she'll make a good dancing partner. She enjoys dancing, she told me."

She seemed to have told him a lot, Jean reflected, but she said nothing more on the subject.

She should be glad, and yet she was unhappy, wretchedly unhappy, Jean reflected as she stood surveying Fred's completed job. She sat down and gazed idly at the flicker of flame that glowed cosily in her new electric fire.

All at once life seemed to stretch out in a long, lonely road in front of her. Her parents were gone, her neighbour was gone and Fred seemed on the point of deserting her. No, she shouldn't use that word ; she had chased him away by refusing to marry him, every time he had asked her·

If he formed an attachment to Marie their friendship couldn't remain as it was, and she would miss his company more than she could say. Maybe he wouldn't care for Marie after all, of course, he was only taking her to a dance.

She kept herself busy during the evenings of the next week so that she wouldn't have time to brood, and there was lots of work to be done between gardening and spring-cleaning.

Fred had often helped her with the garden but he hadn't mentioned it this year and she wouldn't ask him now. He was busy, anyway, with his own work. Suddenly Jean halted in her job, raising her head from the border where she was putting in a row of plants. Could it be that Fred was just trying to let her see what it would be like without his help and companionship? The idea comforted her. Maybe he thought she'd taken him for granted too long, and she had, she admitted to herself.

NEXT Saturday Jean had quite a bit of shopping to do in Karmuir. It was a lovely morning so she walked the half-mile into town, enjoying the spring sunshine.

A red, battered car sped past her shortly after she'd left the house. It was her new neighbour, but he didn't stop to offer her a lift and didn't even wave to her. Well, she'd give him the benefit of the doubt, perhaps he didn't even recognise her. At least he was up at a decent time this morning.

The little country town was busy as usual. Jean went straight to the grocer's and, like most women, she had a good look at the bargains in the window before going in.

Her eyes strayed from one item to another, then she glanced inside. Mr Todd and Marie Bowen were both serving. Yes, Marie was decidedly pretty, with her soft brown hair, pink and white skin and brown, dark-lashed eyes.

Then Jean was conscious of someone looking at her and she shifted her gaze to the other side of the counter to look straight into the eyes of her new neighbour. She was sure he'd been watching her for some time.

How rude he must think her for staring at Marie Bowen!

Jean felt as if he could read her thoughts and colour flamed in her cheeks as she turned away and went into the shop, intending to slip round behind him and among the other customers, but he opened the door as she approached it and they met face to face. He paused to say good morning and Jean knew he had recognised her, but she felt so confused and awkward she merely murmured a brief and almost inaudible answer and walked straight to the other end of the counter.

How stupidly she'd behaved, she told herself, as she left the grocer's and went along the street towards the baker's.

Jean hurried on, absorbed in her own thoughts and oblivious to all around her. The baker's window was as usual an attractive one and she stood there for a minute or so deciding what she should buy. A customer came out and Jean looked round to see her neighbour beside her. He was looking at her hesitantly.

**Clydesdale
Bank
for my money**

" You are my next-door neighbour, aren't you ? " he asked.

Much to Jean's annoyance her cheeks flamed into colour once more. Oh, dear, how uncomfortable she felt.

" I am," she replied in a voice that sounded abrupt.

"Then can I give you a lift home ?" he queried. " My car's right here."

" Oh, no, thank you." Her refusal was instant and very positive. He mustn't think she'd been waiting because of that. " I'm not quite ready," she added lamely. He smiled briefly, lifted his hat and turned towards the kerb.

Jean went into the shop, feeling she'd started off on the wrong foot with her new neighbour. She'd never felt so awkward with anyone before.

When Jean came out his car was gone and she made her way back to the bus stop. She'd been waiting a few minutes when Mr Foster's car turned out of a side street near the baker's and came speeding towards her. She saw a look of surprise flit across his face when he caught sight of her but he didn't slacken speed. So much for getting to know him, Jean reflected miserably. He would think she was a thoroughly unpleasant person, and it was all her own fault.

THE SCHEME OF LIFE

To laugh when a laugh would be cheering,
To comfort when comfort is sought,
To refrain from the habit of sneering;
In a word to do just what we ought,
To treat others the way we'd be treated,
Ah, this is the task that is ours.
If we fail, then God's plan is defeated;
We've wasted the best of our powers.
Not to laugh when a brother is crying,
Nor frown when a neighbour may smile,
To encourage when someone is trying —
Yes, this is the duty worth while.
To be kind and to be sympathetic,
To be brave in the heat of the strife
And never to grow apathetic —
In a word, live a well-balanced life.

EDGAR A. GUEST

JEAN was sitting at lunch that day when she was conscious of an unusual sound near the fireplace. She went quietly over to examine the place from where the noise came and heard a scraping and a distinct chirping.

She tappéd on the new wood built to enclose her tank and the sound ceased. In a few minutes it began again and this time she was certain it was the chirp of a baby bird. But how did it come to be in there ? Could it be trapped ? It certainly sounded in distress.

Jean ran outside to examine the wall near the fireplace, but she couldn't find the tiniest hole that might lead inside. Then she looked up at the chimney and an idea struck her. The bird could have fallen down the chimney and into the space where the watercock for turning off the water was fixed. She rushed inside to have another look, but not before she'd seen a bird swooping about agitatedly, then landing on the roof and uttering cries of distress. That would be the mother bird, she reflected.

The little hole in the inside wall close to the boarding was covered

Remember the real goodness of Farola?

The really natural taste of Farola — you remember
enjoying when you were young — hasn't changed.
No chemicals. No preservatives.
No colouring. And no artificial flavouring.
Today Farola is exactly the same as your grandmother
used. Pure wheat.
With nothing added. And none of the goodness taken
away. It's an extremely versatile base for puddings, cakes
and biscuits — particularly good for infants and invalids.

Write today for free recipe leaflet with 28 exciting recipes to:—

James Marshall (Glasgow) Ltd.,
Blairlinn, Cumbernauld, Glasgow.

Marshalls makes the meal-
Farola, Macaroni, Farolina, Semolina and Ground Rice.

by a small, swinging metal plate about nine inches from the floor. Jean swung it to the side and peered inside, but there was nothing but darkness and silence. Maybe the bird had got out !

She struck a match and in the patch of light she saw one beady eye fixed on her. She knew she was only frightening the poor little thing out of its life, but how could she leave it there to die ? If only someone was there to tell her what to do. If only Mrs Riddock . . . Jean sat back on her heels.

She had a next-door neighbour, she reminded herself and she simply must get help as soon as possible. It didn't matter what he'd think of her.

GORDON FOSTER came to the door and found on his doorstep a dishevelled-looking figure with untidy hair, flushed cheeks and one sleeve rolled up to the elbow. His eyebrows went up in a look of surprise. Was this the standoffish Miss Booth he'd met this morning ?

" Please come and help me," Jean pleaded, pulling unceremoniously at his coat sleeve. " There's a bird stuck in my wall and I can't get it out."

" I'll come," he said without hesitation and strode down the path after the already flying figure.

Jean pointed to the metal plate.

" It's in there," she said.

He put aside the plate and peered in for quite a while.

" You'll need a match." Jean held out a box, but Gordon Foster shook his head.

" No," he said, " it'll scare them. Besides, I've got eyes like a cat. That's what comes of being a bird-watcher and prowling about in the night."

" Oh, I see, so that's what you are !" Jean exclaimed.

" Yes," he said with an amused smile that lit up his face. " I take photographs of them for nature magazines. Haven't you noticed my darkroom ?"

Jean had the grace to blush.

" I have, but I thought . . ." She felt it was too embarrassing to finish her sentence.

" That I was sleeping half the day," stated Gordon Foster calmly. " But look here, I see two fledglings and bits of a nest here. It must have been blown off a chimney-pot and landed here."

" Oh, dear," Jean cried. " I do hope they're not hurt."

" I don't think so." The bird-watcher rose from his knees. " We'll have to coax them out if possible, since I can't put my hand in."

Jean gave him a high wooden stool and two dishes, one with water, one with bread, and he placed the stool on a level with the hole. Then they went outside to give the birds peace to come out.

In the short time they spent outside walking about the garden Jean learned quite a lot about her new neighbour. He was just as keen on gardening as she was and wasn't much older than herself, though his hair

It's unmistakable...
the casual elegance of
hand-made-
to-measure
Scottish clothes

Wouldn't you like to have your clothes made-to-measure ... especially those genuine Scottish tweeds and knitwear classics that depend so much for their elegance on tailoring and fit?

You probably think it would cost a fortune. It needn't.

Thousands of Heather Valley customers expect and demand hand tailored to measure clothes at a lower price than most people expect to pay for stock sizes.

This is just one style in the new Heather Valley of Edinburgh Collection ... beautifully illustrated in our latest brochure. Where you will find a colour-rich choice of 25 tweeds ... with new and exclusive additions for this season. Where you will have a wide choice of hand-crafted knitwear in 18 delightful colours of either Shetland or Lambswool.

If you believe that made-to-measure elegance is important ... if you believe the world's finest tweeds and knitwear come from Scotland ... then our brochure will show you it needn't be expensive. See for yourself, by sending for your free copy of the Heather Valley Brochure.

FINE WOOLLENS WOVEN IN SCOTLAND
PURE NEW WOOL

PURE NEW WOOL

R.S.V.P. **Heather Valley**
OF EDINBURGH

Heather Valley, Dept PFA,
Brunstane Rd.,
Edinburgh EH15 2QL, Scotland.

The People's Friend Annual

was greying. He wasn't a bit grim, but thoughtful-looking with very keen eyes beneath shaggy eyebrows.

And he hadn't ignored her ring at the bell when she went to introduce herself. He'd just stepped into his bath and could do nothing about it.

When they went in again there were two little fledglings fluttering about the living-room.

" They'll be all right," Gordon commented. " They can fly a bit."

He caught them and put them carefully on the window-sill outside and they flew into the lower branches of the nearest tree, where the mother bird flew down to join them.

" That's that, then." Jean turned towards her neighbour, who'd been watching her speculatively.

G ORDON FOSTER smiled but didn't make any remark immediately and Jean was beginning to wonder what was wrong.

" I expect you'll be going to the badminton dance tonight ?" he asked suddenly.

" No," she said. " I usually go, but I'd decided I'd give it a miss this year."

" Won't you change your mind ?" Gordon asked her. " I've been hearing quite a bit about it today. Usually I shop in the city because I get all my photographic equipment there, but I enjoyed my chats with the locals today and they all asked me if I was going to the dance, but I haven't a partner."

It would be hurtful, Jean had thought, seeing Fred with Marie Bowen all evening, and she'd quite decided against it. But if Gordon Foster needed a partner then maybe she should go. Besides, she liked him, and his friendliness this afternoon had somehow eased that lonely feeling that had persisted all week. She'd probably have to get accustomed to seeing Fred and Marie together anyway and the sooner the better.

" I think I will change my mind," she told him with a pleasant smile.

The towering spire watches over the dreaming village.

Think of bedtime with blissful Mohair luxury!

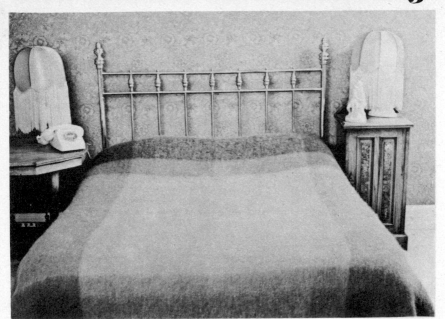

We asked West of Scotland Home Industries to weave a mohair blanket for us—specially for you.

Here it is. 89″ wide and 98″ from fringe-tip to elegant fringe-tip. Sensually silky mohair with a subtle blend of supple fibres* to ensure a long, resilient life.

It's extravagantly lovely, steeped in rich, glowing colour.

Select a multi-hued design in maroon, pansy, deep lilac and crocus (A); bottle green, saxe blue, bold and pale turquoise (B); or chocolate brown, mole, apricot and fawn (C). If you prefer a solid wave of colour, choose from a molten gold (D), a sunset scarlet (E) or an ethereal saxe blue (F).

Astonishingly light, made to swaddle you in cocoon-like cosiness outdoors as well as to cover your bed beautifully, it tucks neatly into a transparent holder for easy carrying.

And how simple to keep in perfect condition! Just a swish through mild suds followed by a lukewarm rinse.

Such a matchless gift for yourself or someone near and dear to you.

The price? Including packing and postage, £25. Perhaps a little more than you're used to spending, but this is much more of a blanket than you're used to finding.

*75% pure mohair, 20% pure new wool and 5% nylon.

Specially manufactured and produced by West of Scotland Home Industries Ltd., Langhaugh Mill, Galashiels, for John McIntyre.

JOHN McINTYRE (Tweeds) LTD
147 HIGH STREET FORT WILLIAM

Changing Partners!

A S she took a long look at herself in the dressing-table mirror,
Dorothy Bell nodded at her calm reflection. Nobody could say
her pride had obviously been badly hurt by the way Brian
Chapman had behaved.

She looked cool and bright enough to deceive anyone, even herself,
in that white linen skirt and blouse, with the white polo-necked jersey.
She brought her tennis racquet out from the cupboard and walked
through to the living-room.

"I'm off to the tennis club for a game, Mum. You can expect me
home about the usual time."

Mrs Bell nodded, clearing the table and fetching a vase of multi-
coloured dahlias to decorate the centre.

by
Fiona
MacLeod

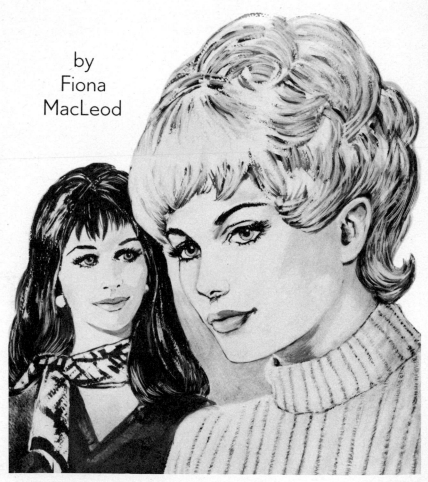

The Royal Dundee Institution For The Blind

Founded 1865

Factory, Offices and Showroom
59 MAGDALEN YARD ROAD, DUNDEE, DD1 4LJ
Phones : Dundee 67292/3 and 60375

Retail Shop
51 NETHERGATE, DUNDEE, DD1 4DQ
Phone: Dundee 24761

A manufacturing and selling organisation employing blind, partially sighted and sighted disabled persons, mainly from the cities of Dundee and Perth and the counties of Angus, Fife, Kinross and Perthshire.

In conjunction with another four similar organisations in Scotland we have traded since 1960 under the name Blindcraft Scotland and Blindcraft products are : Bedding (mattresses, divans, headboards, bed ends, cots, bunk beds, continental quilts and pillows) ; Brushes ; Baskets and Baby Bassinettes in Cane and Willow ; Mats ; Plastic Coated and Galvanised Wirework ; School ; Office and Kitchen Furniture (tubular steel and wooden) ; Woven Fibre (Canetex) and Upholstered Furniture ; and the Dun-di-Donk, our Donkey shaped Pouffee.

This Institution also provides a service for upholstery recovery, the re-caning of chair seats and backs and the re-spraying of cane weave and woven fibre furniture.

Our own transport will collect and deliver free of charge.

L

The People's Friend Annual

" Will you be bringing . . ." she started to ask from force of habit, then suddenly remembered . . . Dorothy's friendship with Brian Chapman was over, ended when the engagement had finally been broken off last week end !

" Oh, Dorothy ! To think he could have done such a thing to you !"

" I suppose I must have been as much to blame as him, Mum. There must have been something about me he didn't like."

But nothing could change the painful fact that she had been jilted for another girl who had taken Brian's fancy.

" You're not playing tennis this afternoon, Dorothy? What if you meet Brian there? You know he likes to play tennis on Saturday afternoons. You don't want to see him again, do you, or are you still hoping you can make it up with him?"

" No, of course not, Mum ! That's the last thing I'm thinking about !" Dorothy hadn't imagined people might consider this was why she was trying to behave normally. " Brian wouldn't have said the things he did if he hadn't been sure."

" That he could do such a thing, Dorothy, and you still seem to think so much of him. I only hope he's ashamed of himself."

It wasn't often her mother showed resentment, but there were signs of it as she talked about Brian. Mum seemed to feel the hurt almost as much as she did !

" But what if you do meet him there, Dorothy ? Do you know what you're going to say to him, what you're going to do ? "

" I'll be as natural as I can, of course. Goodness, Mum, how would you want me to behave? I can't let it ruin my whole life, can I?"

DOROTHY marched smartly down the avenue, looking straight ahead, but feeling a little nervous as she deliberately tried to avoid looking towards Brian's home as she passed it.

Then, just as she was turning the corner at the end of the avenue, she bumped into Mrs Chapman, Brian's mother. Not that Dorothy would have wanted to avoid the older woman, for they had always been friendly. Perhaps that was what made it so awkward

STARS TO GUIDE US

CAN you find the Pole Star in the sky? It's small, but easy to find.

Look to the constellation called the Plough—seven stars that form a box with a tail. A line upwards through the two stars farthest from the tail.

There's the Pole Star! Face it, you're facing north.

Seven stars the signpost to the Pole Star.

And seven virtues, the Bible says, mark the soul that faces God. Faith, hope, charity, prudence, self-restraint, patience and justice to all.

" Seven, too," adds Christ, " are the compassions of such a soul for others."

For the sick, the naked, the hungry and the thirsty, the lost, the lonely and the bereaved.

Rev. T. R. S. Campbell

162

Lovely to live with

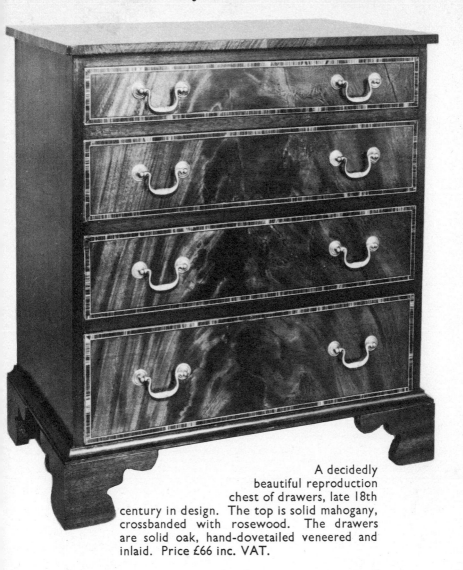

A decidedly
beautiful reproduction
chest of drawers, late 18th
century in design. The top is solid mahogany,
crossbanded with rosewood. The drawers
are solid oak, hand-dovetailed veneered and
inlaid. Price £66 inc. VAT.

The Gateside Mills
CO., LTD.

Gateside, Fife, Scotland
Telephone Strathmiglo 402/3

now. It was their first meeting since the engagement was broken off, and it was difficult to know what to say.

"Hello, Mrs Chapman. It's a nice day, isn't it? I'm just off to the tennis club for a game. I've nothing arranged, but surely someone will be needing a partner. I hope so, anyway."

"Brian will be going there later. I think he's arranged to meet that girl he told you about."

Mrs Chapman obviously found it embarrassing to mention the girl who had come between them, but Dorothy pretended not to notice the older woman's embarrassment.

"Helen Kirkcaldy. Oh, yes, she's a nice girl and a very good player, too. Better than me, anyway."

Mrs Chapman didn't seem to know how to answer this.

"Oh, Dorothy, I'm so sorry that this has happened. I don't know what made Brian do it. I always thought that you and he . . . well, I thought you were right for each other."

"I suppose it was better to realise that it would have been a mistake now, rather than find out later."

"I hope he doesn't discover that he's made a mistake already, Dorothy. I hope he knows what he's doing. He's got a habit of rushing into things that has got him into trouble before, and it's just as likely to do the same again."

Dorothy nodded in quiet agreement. She understood that part of Brian well enough, perhaps she should have understood the rest?

"Well, I suppose I'd better be on my way, Mrs Chapman, if I'm to get to the park. It's always busy on a Saturday afternoon."

But nearly everyone there would have a partner. She might very easily find herself sitting on a seat, forced to watch others enjoying themselves, hoping that someone would take pity on her loneliness and invite her to share a game.

"I hope you won't let this make any difference, Dorothy," suggested Mrs Chapman with a restrained anxiety. "We can still be friends. You know you're always welcome, as far as I'm concerned. I was going to be showing you that recipe for cheese scones. Would you still like to have it?"

A S she walked along the pleasant, tree-lined road, Dorothy could see that the tennis courts were busy, although not completely filled with players.

She passed through the entrance gate and along the path which led towards the clubhouse. A few people that she knew sat around, watching the play or chatting.

Dorothy smiled.

"Is anyone trying to arrange a game?" she asked brightly.

But it seemed they were all either waiting for some special partner to appear, or had already been playing and were resting after their efforts.

Trying to ignore the disappointment which crept over her at this discouraging first reception, Dorothy went into the dressing-room.

It wasn't completely empty, but the only person there was the girl she would have wanted to avoid, Helen Kirkcaldy.

But Helen's expressionable face flamed up selfconsciously. Troubled blue eyes betrayed the fact that her feelings were not so very different from Dorothy's!

" I thought I might find someone here who would give me a game," Dorothy explained quickly. " But there's nobody yet. Perhaps I'm too early."

" Dorothy . . ." She turned as the other girl said her name. " I'm not very good at behaving as though nothing has happened. I didn't deliberately try to come between you and Brian, you do understand that, don't you? It was something I couldn't help."

What did Helen Kirkcaldy expect her to say? That she understood perfectly and forgave her completely for the hurtful thing she had done?

" I wish we could be friends, Dorothy. I know I shouldn't really expect that, but it would be nice, wouldn't it? What do you say? Please !"

Dorothy hesitated only because she had paused to think about it. Not for the first time she had been asking herself what had made Brian do this to her.

This little conversation with Helen had offered a possible answer. Nice, that's it ! She's a really nice person at heart, isn't she? I believe I could almost like her myself if I took the trouble to try ! Is she so much nicer than I usually am?

It was too late now to improve her picture in Brian's eyes, but was there any harm in trying to improve your image with everybody else? Why not show them. . . .

A S Dorothy walked outside into the sunshine, chatting with the other girl, she saw Brian glancing about him, evidently searching for some sign of Helen.

As he caught sight of the two girls together, Dorothy felt like laughing at his confusion. But that wouldn't have been nice of her, would it? So she simply allowed herself a quiet smile, which was meant to suggest there was no reason for anyone to feel embarrassed about the situation.

" Dorothy was looking for a game, Brian," Helen suggested with an anxious eagerness. " I thought we might find a partner to make up a foursome. I see Duncan there, he's just come in at the gate."

" Yes, I noticed him coming from the other direction when I came in. I think he was hanging back when he caught sight of me."

Helen looked at him hesitantly. There was no law to prevent anyone being there, if they were a member.

" Do you think we could invite him to be Dorothy's partner? Would you like to ask him . . ."

It would have been the easiest thing for Dorothy to protest she didn't want Duncan for a partner. Certainly, he hadn't been engaged to Helen, but he had been her recognised boy friend before . . . before Brian had stepped in to come between them. There had been chances of seeing and talking to him on other occasions, but she hadn't paid particular attention to him before.

'not to be taken before meals'

Lees'

BIG
MACAROON
BAR
best value for
5p

POPULAR 2½p SIZE ALSO AVAILABLE

" I'll ask him, if you're sure you want me to, Helen? I suppose he can only refuse. Is that all right with you, Dorothy?"

Dorothy had to smile to herself later. It should have been an embarrassing meeting for all of them, and to begin with it had been, but everybody had so obviously been most anxious to be pleasant to everyone else.

In fact, it was really very surprising just how enjoyable the afternoon turned out to be, no less for Dorothy than for her three companions.

She had never really known Duncan Steele very well before their game. True, she had met him occasionally at parties and dances, or around the tennis club, when she had exchanged a few friendly words, and had even danced with him now and again when chance had brought them together, but that had not been often. She had always thought him pleasant enough, but quiet and rather serious-minded.

However, as the match progressed and the players began to feel less and less embarrassed about the situation, she discovered that Duncan was actually quite a lot of fun to be with, with his wry sense of humour and boyish grin.

So well had things gone for them during the game that they all went together afterwards to a nearby cafe where they ordered long, cool drinks all round, and sat a long time over them, laughing and chatting happily Indeed, by the time the group broke up, each of them to go to their respective homes for tea, it was quite clear that any ill feelings which might still have lingered between the various parties had completely disappeared, and they all agreed to arrange a return match the following week.

Dorothy found herself feeling strangely pleased that she had a firm date to see Duncan again, and, as she made her way home, she wondered if she was perhaps now well on her way to recovering from her broken heart.

She rather thought she was . . .

Dim echoes of the past find peace at length.

Grey hair?

AMAZING PROVEN TREATMENT BRINGS BACK NATURAL LOOKING COLOUR IN ONLY 3 WEEKS

*
Also
Formula 16
Shampoo—
for mature
hair.
Only 16p
a bottle.
*

In only three weeks you can look years younger. Formula 16 is a safe, scientific treatment already proven by thousands. It brings back natural looking colour. And because it works gradually, the change in your appearance is also gradual, not an embarrassing sudden difference.

Formula 16 is pleasantly non-greasy. Conditions the hair, too, and is successful with both men and women.

Just apply a few drops to the scalp each day. Colour will feed back into the grey. The hair also becomes easier to manage. And within three weeks you can look and feel a confidently different, younger person. After this, just one application of Formula 16 a week is all it takes to keep the new outlook it has given you.

Prove for yourself that grey hair can be a thing of the past. Buy a bottle of Formula 16 and see how nice and easy it is. From chemists, hairdressers and stores. A well-spent £1.13.

A VINCENT PRODUCT

Formula 16

L E Vincent & Partners Ltd   Kings House 10 Haymarket London SW1

By
CHRISTINE MAXWELL

New Year At The Cottage

IT stood at the far end of a winding Border glen . . . an isolated little
cottage which had been built many years ago for a shepherd and
which had always seemed a real home in spite of its lonely position.
Children had been born there, growing to play beside the young
River Tweed which trickled past. Capable housewives had kept the
place in shining order, and in former days the two miles to the nearest
village had bothered no one.

The People's Friend Annual

But times change, and at length the little cottage found itself deserted. For the first time for seventy years no wisps of smoke went drifting upwards from the chimney and the door stood closed. To a stranger who might chance on the glen road it no longer presented a hospitable welcoming appearance. It was just one more abandoned cottage.

"But why won't your new shepherd live in it?" Susan Forrest questioned her uncle when spending the autumn holiday weekend at the Border farm near the other end of the glen. "Dave Laurie was there thirty years and found it all right."

The farmer nodded.

"True enough, lass, but it's a young chap I've got in Dave's place. He wouldn't go to the cottage and he's found himself a house in the village."

"Maybe you can't blame him." The farmer's wife sighed. "As he says, with his car he can be at the head of the glen in ten minutes."

"With his car!" snorted John Turnbull. "At his age I had to walk everywhere."

"All the same, you wouldn't like to do without your car now," his wife pointed out with a smile.

"I wouldn't like to do without my one anyway," Susan said. "It's so easy getting down here with it, and I like having a breath of fresh Border air every so often."

Mrs Turnbull beamed at her.

"We like having you, dear," she said warmly.

And it was true. Susan had been a welcome visitor since she had first come as a child. What a pretty girl she was now, mused the older woman as she looked at the oval face framed so attractively by golden brown hair, and with a pair of deep brown eyes set in it.

YET Susan didn't seem in her usual spirits this weekend. She had been quiet since her arrival the previous evening, and the news about the old cottage seemed to depress her unduly.

Surely an old cottage being abandoned couldn't matter all that much to a girl with an interesting, responsible job in a big city. Mrs Turnbull's brow furrowed as she studied the girl uneasily.

Presently Susan had another question to ask.

"What will you do with the cottage, Uncle John?" she inquired. "Will you let it to someone?"

John Turnbull shook his head.

"Who would want it? No, it'll have to come down. There's no use leaving it for vandals to find one of these days."

Susan gave an exclamation of dismay.

"Oh, Uncle John! Must it really come down? I can't bear to think of it, for ever since I've come here a visit to the cottage has been something to look forward to."

"It's empty now, my dear," the farmer reminded her. "It isn't the same as when Mrs Laurie was there, with her welcome for all you young folk, and the good things she gave you to eat."

172

FOR COUNTRY HOLIDAYS IN BRITAIN!

FARM HOLIDAY GUIDE lists county by county, Britain's best farm houses, country guest houses, village inns, small country hotels, children's holidays, pony trekking, fishing, shooting, inland cruising, camping and caravanning holidays.

MORE THAN 3,000 PERSONALLY RECOMMENDED REVIEWS
Illustrated throughout

600 pages of interesting and helpful information : fullest details of terms, food, location amenities. A happy guide to cheerful hospitality which includes many friendly halts for bed and breakfast.

For the ideal country holiday at moderate rates, send today for

THE FARM HOLIDAY GUIDE

Price 25p   (*postage 13½p extra*)

" What I liked best was our Hogmanay visits," recalled Susan. " It was such fun to go tramping away up there in the middle of the night, then waiting till we could hear the church clock strike in the distance. After that the door would be opened and what a wonderful welcome we'd get ! Oh, I do wish the Lauries hadn't gone away to live in Dumfries !"

But it was inevitable that the time would come for an elderly shepherd to retire. No one could wonder at Davie and his wife going to enjoy their retirement with a married daughter who had a roomy house in Dumfries. They couldn't go on for ever !

It was just a pity when pleasant things came to an end.

And now Susan found her thoughts turning to her life in Edinburgh, and her spare-time work with a company of Girl Guides. Some of the older girls were so keen on outdoor things that they had begged her to arrange a weekend camp for them sometime during the winter.

" When the trees are bare and nothing is growing it would all be so different," Mavis Oliver had said eagerly. " If there was snow just think of the bird and animal tracks we could learn about. Please, Captain, do fix up something."

Susan hadn't made any promises. But now an idea came into her mind and she turned to her uncle.

" Uncle John, would you let me bring three or four of my Guides to camp in the cottage during the Christmas holidays?"

Mr and Mrs Turnbull stared in amazement.

" Camp in the cottage? You're daft, lass," said the farmer bluntly. " The place won't be fit for living in by then."

" Yes, it will," Susan argued. " We only need somewhere for shelter, and we could keep warm by having a fire in the old grate. You wouldn't like to think of us out in tents, would you, at that time of year?"

" Why not come to the farm?" asked Mrs Turnbull hospitably. " If you didn't want to stay in the house you could have the big barn."

Susan shook her head.

" It's kind of you, Auntie," she said gratefully. " But if we were there you'd be slipping us food ! We really do want to rough it a little."

" I still think you're daft," grumbled John Turnbull. " You just don't want me to set the men on to knock down the cottage."

" Yes, that's it." Susan smiled back.

D RIVING home to Edinburgh two days later, Susan thought how pleased the girls would be to hear everything had been arranged. A brief visit to the old cottage had revealed that there were several useful bits of old furniture—a table, some chairs and other small items the former occupants hadn't wanted to take with them.

There was also a little coal in the lean-to shed at the end of the building, and Uncle John had said they could use it and welcome. If only the weather stayed fine ! If only the glen wasn't deep in snow by that time, thought Susan with a moment's unease.

Surely it would be all right? Every visit she'd paid to the farm in winter had coincided with a spell of mild weather. Now her thoughts drifted back across the years, and she tried to recall the names of all the

They will still need your help in 2001

In 30 years from now when man's ingenuity has made space travel to the moon and perhaps farther a commonplace event there will still be sick and disabled ex-Servicemen waiting for a place in Erskine Hospital.

As a disabled man gets older his disabilities often become more troublesome and the relatives who have looked after him become less fit. It is then that the specialised facilities that ERSKINE HOSPITAL can offer become necessary. Sometimes the devoted relatives have to take on other responsibilities and commitments, making it difficult for them to care for the invalid.

Erskine Hospital is not nationalised and so it depends on your generosity to provide treatment and care for the 350 ex-Service patients who cannot help themselves. They have done their bit. Maybe you have, too. Will you do a bit more and help them? Please.

Donations should be sent to the Treasurer, G. A. Rankin, 201 West George Street, Glasgow C.2. Legacies, on which the hospital depends so much, should be made in favour of "*The Princess Louise Scottish Hospital for Limbless Sailors and Soldiers*".

children she'd played with who had grown up, then usually left the district.

She'd had brief, close friendships with many of the girls. The boys had been teases, always up to some mischief. How she'd regretted each time her holiday came to an end, knowing it would be months, maybe a year before she would see any of these young friends again.

It was strange how one could be so friendly with companions at the age of eight or ten, and fourteen years later not even know what had become of them.

There were the Duncans . . . the Bairds . . . the Wests, thought Susan. Even Auntie doesn't know where they all are now.

She drove on steadily towards Edinburgh. The nearer she got, the more unwelcome thoughts pressed in on her. She'd tried so hard all week-end to forget what had happened earlier in the month, but it was useless. Even while she recalled past names to herself she couldn't shut out the memory of Philip Sloan's gay blue eyes and his breath-taking smile.

SPRING TIDE

At Kinlochbervie where the sea-pinks
   grow
   Green bracken shoots spring from
   their bed of brown ;
The mountains tall frown on the loch
   below,
   And melting snow in quiet streams
   flows down.

At Kinlochbervie when the boats
   come in
   Laden with silver harvest from the
   deep,
Their escort is a crowd of hungry
   gulls
   Who wake with raucous cries the
   hillsides steep.

How eagerly the young men leap
   ashore !
   Strong shoulders take the strain of
   heaving creels ;
Herrings are loaded, lorries driven
   away,
   And back on to the loch the silence
   steals.

MARY CONNEL

"KEEP the holiday Monday free for me, darling," he'd begged her. "We'll have a jaunt somewhere. All right by you?"

"Yes, of course, Philip," she'd replied happily.

For six months Philip and she had been seeing each other constantly. He was such an amusing companion. When he looked into her eyes Susan felt her heart throb, and when he kissed her, life seemed rosy and wonderful.

Working in adjoining offices, they met often. It wasn't long before everyone in Susan's office knew of the romance and other girls envied Susan . . . all except Brenda Tait, who grew silent each time Philip Sloan was mentioned.

It was Brenda who brought everything crashing down in ruins. Early last week there had been chatter about plans for the autumn holiday, and Susan had said blithely she didn't yet know where she'd be going that day.

M.

The People's Friend Annual

" Somewhere with the boy friend, of course," Maisie Brown had joked good-naturedly, bringing a blush to Susan's cheeks.

When it was time to go home that evening Brenda Tait had lingered.

" Susan," she said awkwardly. " Are you really going out with Philip Sloan next Monday? I mean . . . are you sure he isn't going away for the whole weekend?"

Susan had stared. She longed to tell Brenda to mind her own business. Instead, she said coldly that Philip had asked her to keep the day free for an outing.

Brenda looked back uneasily, then seemed to take a decision.

" Susan, you'll have to know. Philip is engaged to my cousin who lives over in Glasgow. He's a flirt, if ever there was one, and May knows it, but once they're married she'll keep him in order."

Susan's heart had pounded as she answered still more coldly that she didn't believe what Brenda was saying.

How could she believe it, remembering Philip's kisses, his whispered words of admiration? Anyway, when they met that evening she'd tell him what Brenda had said. They'd have a laugh over the way people gossipped.

It hadn't turned out that way at all, she remembered bitterly. Philip had grown red, then he had burst out in a tirade against people who kept on interfering. Pulling her close, he had confessed that it was true he was engaged to May Tait, but they wouldn't be married for ages.

" Until then you and I can have lots of fun," he'd said lightly.

He had gone on to explain that he had known May Tait for years. Her father was head of a big business similar to the one he worked in at present, and there was talk of finding him a job there one of these days. After all, Glasgow was really his home town.

So Susan Forrest had just been a suitable girl with whom to pass the time during his stay in Edinburgh ! When she got her breath back, Susan told Philip just what she thought. A quarrel had followed, and they had parted in disillusionment.

" I never imagined you were a prim Victorian type," Philip had taunted.

" And I never thought you were mean and disloyal," she countered.

What scalding tears of humiliation she had wept into her pillow that night ! But why dwell on it now? Once more Susan strove to think of other things . . . her enjoyable stay at the Border farmhouse, the Guide meeting tomorrow, anything to help her to forget how Philip had let her down.

IT was certainly cheering next evening to find how pleased the girls were by the prospect of a country weekend later on.

" Let's go for New Year, shall we?" Mavis Oliver asked. " That would be fun."

" Oh, yes, let's go then," cried the three other girls who were to be in the small group.

Susan was surprised. She'd thought they would have had things

178

The safe way to the top

Safety and quality. The two things you look for when you want to buy a ladder.

They're the first two things you find when you consider a Ramsay. And it doesn't stop there.

Take the A1 Model Loft Ladder. It's made completely of lightweight aluminium and disappears in seconds. The non-slip treads are 3½" wide with a 1" nosing and are fitted at a standard 10" rise. And we can supply a safety handrail if required.

RAMSAY
BRITAIN'S FINEST LADDER

Registered Office and Works:
61 West High Street,
FORFAR, Angus, DD8 1BH.
Phone FORFAR 0307-2255
Grams: "Ladders, Forfar"

Edinburgh Depot:
B.R.S DEPOT,
60 Jane Street,
Leith, EDINBURGH,
EH6 5HT.
Ph. 031-554 2822

Glasgow Depot:
KELVINBRIDGE YARD,
South Woodside Road (off Great
Western Road), GLASGOW,
G4 9HE.
Phone 041-339 3083

ALSO AT LONDON AND LEEDS

The only can that's backed by a guarantee

"Made from finest Scotch Beef blended with choice Belfast Ham". That's our personal guarantee on the back of every can of A & B Roll. Who else dare make such a claim. Open it up and taste for yourself.

GRANT BROS. (MEAT CANNERS) **LTD.**
706 GARSCUBE ROAD, GLASGOW NW
TELEPHONE: 041-332 8111

going on at home at that time. For herself, she'd be only too glad to escape the usual New Year festivities. No, she didn't feel in tune with that sort of thing at the moment.

" I must write and fix the date with Uncle John at once," she decided. " Then he won't start pulling down the cottage just yet."

It was nice to think that once more there would be life in the place when Hogmanay came.

And fortunately, as so often in the past, the weather stayed open when the time did come along. There was sunshine on the day Susan drove the four girls over the familiar road to the Borders. If it lasted they would be able to have lots of outdoor activities during their stay.

The girls were all in high spirits. They loved the cottage at once, small as it seemed to them.

" Why, there are only two rooms !" exclaimed Mavis Oliver. " It's a real but and ben."

" Where did people sleep in it?" Jill Gray wanted to know. " You said a family lived here, Captain, but I can't think how they managed."

Susan described how it had been when the Lauries lived there. A big bed had stood in the living-room recess, and the sons had slept in the other room. It hadn't seemed cramped, it was just the way country folk lived in the past.

" It's certainly cosy," exclaimed Glynis Grant when a good fire had been started and Susan had lit the paraffin lamp she'd borrowed from her aunt. " This really is fun."

By ten o'clock everyone was warmly tucked up in a sleeping bag. Only Susan remained awake for some time.

How quiet it was here ! No traffic, none of the inevitable sounds there are in a city, just a complete silence. Suppose she did hear a sound . . . a footstep, perhaps? What would she feel then? A faint doubt came into her mind. They were really very alone up here, and the girls were her responsibility. But Uncle John had seemed to think they would be all right. On that reassuring thought, Susan at last fell asleep.

FORTUNATELY, the weather stayed mild. Useful nature work was done on the lower part of the hills during the next two days, then all at once it was the last day of the year. By special invitation the campers went to have tea in the farmhouse. Mrs Turnbull had insisted on that.

And what a tea ! The girls did justice to all the good things prepared for them, chattering and laughing to the elderly couple as if they were lifelong friends.

After tea, Susan's aunt took her aside.

" Susan, I'd better warn you," she whispered. " Your uncle means to drive up and first foot you later on. He wants it to be a surprise, but I thought you might get a scare if you heard anyone at the door at that time of night."

" Thanks, Auntie." Susan smiled. " I won't tell the girls and I'll try to be suitably surprised when he arrives. Are you coming, too?"

Angus MacIntyre, Royal Scots Fusiliers. Blinded Belgium, 1944. Who cares?

Angus was born in Ayrshire during the First War. Like many of his generation, he volunteered for the territorials and was mobilised in 1939 to fight in the Second. And while in Belgium, he was one of a group given the unenviable task of probing a German minefield. A blinding explosion brought Angus's eyesight to an abrupt end. After many months in military hospitals, he was brought to Linburn. Angus is now settled happily with his wife and family. But he still needs help. Your help. Please care as much as you can for Angus — and his fellow war blinded ex-servicemen. A donation, legacy or deed of covenant is the most positive way of remembering their sacrifice.

SCOTTISH WAR BLINDED

SCOTTISH NATIONAL INSTITUTION FOR THE WAR BLINDED

38 Albany Street, Edinburgh EH1 3PW
also at Queen's Crescent, Glasgow C4 and Linburn, Midlothian.

Mrs Turnbull nodded.

" I haven't missed first-footing at the cottage in thirty years." She beamed. " It'll be a little after midnight when we arrive, for your uncle won't stir out of the house till the New Year has come."

" I've agreed with the girls that they can sit up and listen to the radio programme," Susan told her. " So we'll all be awake."

With an effort the girls managed to stay awake until it was close on midnight. Then they threw off their drowsiness.

" Captain, at home we always open the door when it's going to be twelve," Jill Gray announced. " Shouldn't we do that here?"

" Don't open it wide," Susan instructed. " The house will soon get cold if you do."

What a lot of superstitions there were about the New Year, she thought. The door must be open at midnight. A dark man must be first to cross the threshold after that, and he should have a lump of coal with him for luck. Susan found herself wondering vaguely about the origins of this and all the other traditions and superstitions connected with this peculiarly Scottish celebration.

She hoped that her aunt and uncle would arrive soon after twelve to first-foot the cottage, for the girls were impatient to greet them and discover what they had brought as gifts.

Just then, there was a cry of surprise from one of the Guides.

GOODNESS, what had happened? Her musings were broken into as Jill Gray rushed into the room, her face white as a sheet.

" Oh, Captain, there's a man out there!" she gasped. " I looked out when I opened the door and he was standing at the other window. Is he trying to break in, do you think? What'll we do?" she panted.

A man? Some stranger? Susan fought back her own sense of panic. No, it hadn't been wise to come to this lonely spot. It would be some time yet before her uncle appeared, so they were at the mercy of anyone who was really out to make trouble.

But she'd got to do something. Telling the girls to keep very quiet, she tiptoed through to the other room. It was in darkness, so she ventured to peep from the window.

Jill was right ! She could just make out the figure of a tall man now moving away from the window. Where was he going? Round to the back, perhaps, where there was another door and window?

The thumping of her heart almost suffocated Susan. She stood hesitating, then suddenly she heard the familiar creak of the door of the shed where the coal was kept.

What was the man doing there? She simply must know. Moving to the outer door, she opened it silently and looked out. There was just enough starlight to see the man bending down as if to creep inside the shed.

Was he looking for shelter? Then why hadn't he knocked and asked for it sensibly. No, he must be up to no good, creeping about like that, plainly trying not to be heard.

A suit for all seasons

The GLENCAIRN is available ready-made in a good range of sizes, or you can have it made to your own measurements, in one of our beautiful 100% pure wool tweeds, or blended tweeds.

It is, we feel, one of the most attractive suits you could buy anywhere and is extremely reasonably priced.

We have a large selection of other high fashion garments — Coats, Skirts, Kilts, Dresses and Knitwear — either ready-to-wear or made-to-measure. Get a copy of our free colour brochure now and a selection of patterns!

Write to MOFFAT WEAVERS, Dept. PFA, Freepost, Moffat, Dumfriesshire or phone Moffat 20134.

(We pay postage — you don't even need a stamp.)

If he goes right inside I could shut the door on him, thought Susan nervously. It would only be till Uncle John got here, but it would mean we would be safe. Dare I do it?

Hardly breathing, she stole right outside and along the side of the cottage. Yes, the man was right into the shed now, and the light from a torch he held was flickering around the small heap of coal in one corner.

At any moment he might swing round . . . it really was now or never. Springing forward, Susan slammed shut the door and shot home the bolt. She didn't wait to hear more than a startled exclamation as she turned and fled to the cottage door.

The girls were huddled together in alarm, their eyes like saucers.

" Oh, Captain, where have you been?" they chorused. " Did you see the man?"

" I—I've shut him into the coal shed," stammered Susan.

Now she found herself trembling all over. It had been a nerve-wracking moment. But help would soon be here, for now she could hear the welcome sound of Big Ben striking midnight on Jill's little transistor.

" It's New Year!" exclaimed Mavis. " Happy New Year, Captain!"

Quite recovered from their fright, the girls exchanged greetings. Jill ran again to open the door, coming back giggling.

" Oh, Captain, the man's fairly shouting!" she exclaimed. " He's calling for someone. It sounds like ' Dave '!"

A sudden dismay came to Susan and she hurried to listen.

" Dave? Are you there, Dave?" she heard from the shed. " You've locked me in, man."

Oh, no ! Surely this couldn't be some friend of the Lauries who didn't know they had left? But it must be. Why else would he shout Dave in that manner?

" Isn't he making a noise?" Mavis Oliver laughed in an unconcerned manner. " He must be furious !"

Susan swallowed.

" I think there's been a mistake," she got out. " Wait inside, girls, till I see."

WHEN she reached the end of the cottage it was plain that the prisoner was now doing his best to kick the door open. With her hand on the bolt, Susan hesitated. Then she called out a question.

" Are—are you looking for Dave Laurie?" she faltered.

There was a sudden silence, then an aggrieved voice replied.

" Of course I am ! Isn't he here? Who's speaking, anyway?"

Gradually, Susan was becoming more and more convinced that she had misjudged their mysterious night visitor, and that the stranger was in fact a friend of the Lauries, who, not having heard that they were no longer living there, had come all the way out to the cottage to pay them a surprise visit on Hogmany.

She was now beginning to feel decidedly apologetic about her behaviour towards their unexpected guest, and looked forward with some trepida-

tion to having to face him and explain her mistake, especially since he sounded so angry and indignant.

But there was nothing for it now but to open the door and face the music, and that he would lend a sympathetic ear to her explanations. After all, he had given all the girls quite a fright by his strange behaviour.

SUSAN pulled back the bolt. The man who emerged was tall and young. In the shadowy light from the torch he still held she could see a pair of dark eyes looking at her in astonishment.

" Who are you?" he repeated. " Where's Dave Laurie?"

" The Lauries left some months ago," Susan replied. " I'm staying here for the week-end with some Girl Guides."

" Dave's left?" exclaimed the stranger. " I never knew that. And does the farmer know you're staying here?"

" Yes, of course. He's my uncle."

" Your uncle?" The torch shone full in her face. " Why, then, you must be Susan Forrest ! Is that right?"

How on earth did he know her? It was Susan's turn to stare. She certainly didn't know him . . . not even when they moved into the light which shone from the open cottage door. She looked doubtfully back at these dark eyes and the rather plain, pleasant face of the tall young man, still unable to think who he could be.

" Don't you remember me, Susan?" he asked. " I used to stay in the village. I was one of the gang of kids that played together, and when you came on holiday we let you join us."

Of course she remembered that ! But which of the boys had he been? All at once it came to her.

" You're Alan Baird," she exclaimed. " Yes, I remember now."

What a tease he had been in these past days when they were all children together ! Yet how sympathetic he had been the day he found her weeping over the death of a pet lamb on the farm. She'd always liked him after that, and had been sorry when he and his parents moved away from the village.

They looked at each other and Susan's colour rose. What a way to renew an old friendship ! She tried to apologise for what she had done.

" I thought you were some intruder," she told him.

" No wonder." He grinned forgivingly. " You see, I've just started a new job in Edinburgh, and I'm so much on my own that things are a bit dull. I thought it would be fun to drive down and first-foot the Lauries again, never imagining they would be away. As I was too early, I left my car a bit down the glen and was waiting about till it was midnight."

" But what were you doing in the coal shed?" asked Susan.

" Oh, you know the old tradition about a first foot having a lump of coal in his hand as he enters. I hadn't brought any, but I knew where it was kept and that Dave wouldn't mind being given a bit of his own coal."

How simple the explanation was once it was given ! Susan smiled again, then made a suggestion.

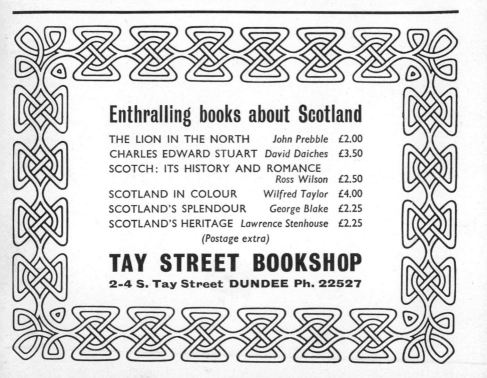

The People's Friend Annual

" Why not come in and be our first foot?" she asked Alan Baird. " Uncle John won't mind, for he knows that before he got grey he wasn't dark in the least ! Perhaps you'll bring good luck to the cottage. It's due to be pulled down soon, you know," she ended sadly.

" I must hear about that," said Alan. " And I'd like to have your Edinburgh address, please, Susan."

" Yes, of course," Susan replied.

Leading the way inside, she didn't after all think that one of her New Year resolutions would be never again to get friendly with any young man !

It was really very strange how she had become attracted to the stranger so soon after their first meeting for years, Susan thought— especially after a meeting so inauspicious as theirs had been !

But nonetheless she was very glad Alan Baird had came back so un- expectedly into her life, and the prospect of seeing him again in Edin- burgh, and perhaps being taken out by him, was very pleasing indeed.

ALL that happened last Hogmanay. Now it's coming up to another one, and the little cottage is still standing in its lonely glen.

It hardly knows itself now, with all the modern improvements which have been made inside. Only the rugged outer walls are the same. And when it is New Year there will be smoke drifting up from the chimney.

Yes, it was a good idea to turn it into one of these places so sought after by city dwellers, where they can relax in peace after the bustle of town. What could John Turnbull do but agree to sell it to the young man who became engaged to his niece? Hadn't the romance really begun at the old cottage, that Hogmanay night when Susan locked Alan Baird in the coal shed?

So it's pretty certain that for many more Hogmanays there will be life and first-footing going on at the cottage.

A gentle ending to your perfect day.

Printed and Published by D. C. Thomson & Co., Ltd., 12 Fetter Lane, Fleet Street, London, E.C.4.